Mrs. Flyn

Christmas

FRANCES MACKAY

Christmas

Published by Scholastic Publications Ltd,
Villiers House,
Clarendon Avenue,
Leamington Spa,
Warwickshire CV32 5PR

Author Frances Mackay
Editor Christine Lee
Sub-editor Jane Wright
Series designer Joy White
Designers Joy White and Lynne Joesbury
Illustrations Tony O'Donnell, Liz Thomas, Joanne Boden
Cover illustration Frances Lloyd
Cover photograph Martyn Chillmaid

Designed using Aldus Pagemaker
Processed by Pages Bureau, Leamington Spa
Artwork by Steve Williams Design, Leicester
Printed in Great Britain by Clays Ltd, Bungay, Suffolk

British Library Cataloguing-in-Publication Data
A catalogue record for this book is
available from the British Library.

ISBN 0-590-53039-9

Dedicated to my Grandparents

Contents

Introduction

This book aims to provide a rich variety of activities on the Christmas theme. The activities have been produced to save the teacher valuable time and have been designed to cater for the wide range of age and ability levels found within primary schools.

The book has been divided into sections according to subject areas: English, mathematics, science, geography, history, technology and craft, as well as a general section. Religious education forms a major strand throughout each subject and does not, therefore, have a separate section devoted to it. The religious education aspects refer only to the Christian faith, but many of the worksheets may be appropriate, or can be adapted, to other religions and can, therefore, be used as valuable comparative exercises.

Each page comprises a photocopiable worksheet that the children can use themselves. The sheets are ordered in level of ability in each section. Where appropriate, references to National Curriculum Attainment Targets and Levels have also been incorporated in the Teachers' Notes.

❑ Denotes ideas for extension activities.

English

Dear Santa (AT3) Letters can be displayed on the wall, made into a book or posted off to Santa.

Rudolph's Christmas (AT3) This activity allows the children to assume another identity and consider a different point of view.

Christmas writing paper (AT3) This page allows the children to write their own stories or poems.

Christmas storyboard (AT3) This page can be attempted at various levels and enables children to plan and structure their story. Use this idea with familiar stories to develop the concept of narrative sequence. The drawings should help the children to describe the characters and scenes in more detail.

Christmas in my house (AT3) Children can use this page to help them write about Christmas in their homes.

❑ Display completed pages or make a house-shaped book.

Christmas ABC (AT3, AT4) Enlarge the sheet to allow more writing space.

❑ Letter outlines can be traced on to an overhead projector sheet and the enlarged shapes used to form a mural.

My best Christmas (AT3) Begin by discussing the children's ideas and experiences. The word bank will be useful for spelling and providing a a stimulus for the children's creative writing.

Christmas carol puzzle (AT2) Solution: Silent night.

❑ Let the children make up their own puzzles. This will help reinforce initial letter sounds.

Christmas puzzle (AT2/2; AT3/2) The picture and word clues make this activity suitable for very young and less able children.

The sounds of Christmas (AT1, AT3) Link this activity to science work on sounds. Record the sounds on tape. Encourage the children to suggest a variety of answers and to choose the most appropriate.

❑ Ask the children to write a poem incorporating these sounds.

Christmas acrostics (AT1, AT3, AT4) The children may need practice with group acrostics before doing their own. Encourage the use of dictionaries to provide word ideas.

Christmas (AT3) This activity enables the children to sort out ideas about Christmas and provides an incentive to research further. This activity will relate well to history work.

Shaped poems (AT3) Make a class poem first to stimulate ideas.

Match the crackers (AT1, AT2, AT4) Encourage the use of dictionaries and discussion of words with several meanings.

❑ Ask the children to find other words and definitions and make more 'crackers'.

Christmas words (AT3/3)

❑ Make an exciting display by getting the children to make larger reproductions of their words and colour them in.

'S' word crossword (AT2, AT3) Solution:
Across – 2. star, 5. stable, 6. sing, 7. shelter.
Down – 1. Santa, 2. surprise, 4. sleigh, 5. spirit.

❑ Go on to use words with the same initial letters or blends and endings. The children could make up their own crossword or investigate alliteration.

Christmas comic strip (AT3) This will encourage reluctant writers to produce a story. The children will need to study the drawings and make inferences to tell the story. Ask them to share their stories. Are the same conclusions drawn?

The first Christmas (AT3) Ask the children to write sentences underneath each scene, then cut out the pictures and put them back together again in the correct sequence.

❑ Mini-books could also be made.

Find another word (AT1, AT4) This activity encourages the use of the dictionary and the thesaurus. Compare everyone's answers to see how many different words there are with the same or similar meanings.

❑ The words could be mounted on card to build up a word bank.

De-coding Christmas messages (AT2) Use this rebus puzzle to introduce work on codes – an excellent way to practise skills of inference, prediction and comprehension

Christmas word fun (AT3/ 3; AT4/3) Scrambled words: decorations, lights, present, manger, stable, shepherd. Discuss the strategies for unscrambling the words. There may be several possible answers; encourage the children to discuss which one is most appropriate. Let them use dictionaries for the sentences and for finding words from the letters in 'Merry Christmas'.

❑ Let the children make up their own scrambled words list. Add them to your word bank.

Christmas word search (AT2/2) This aids familiarity with common Christmas words.

❑ Encourage the children to devise their own word search.

The story of Christmas (AT2/3; AT3/3) This puzzle is based on the Biblical story of the birth of Jesus and can, therefore, be used to reinforce work in RE. Missing words: eve, Jesus, star, stable, Mary, Joseph, inn, wise men, east, new, king, son, God, frankincense, myrrh, swaddling, clothes, manger.

Christmas word puzzle (AT3) This activity encourages trial and error and deductive thinking.

❑ Ask the children to try out puzzles of their own using squared paper.

A Christmas tale (AT2/3) Children should share their answers as several words may be appropriate. Comprehension of the passage will become apparent in their drawings. Possible missing words: night, noise, looked, who, standing, wore, were, toes, father, father, man, need, said, bag, kittens, tail, eye, man.

❑ Invite the children to write their own short stories and delete certain words. Encourage them to try to fill in each other's stories.

Maths

How many? (AT2/1)

❑ Find out how many in the class have these toys and then ask the children make a simple picture graph of the results.

Gingerbread men (AT2/1) This page can be enlarged to allow the children to draw the buttons more easily.

Colours (AT2/1) This page can be enlarged to make colouring easier.

2 more than (AT2/2) Some children may need to use counters to help them.

The twelve days of Christmas 1 & 2 (AT2/2&3)

❑ This could form the basis for a large mural of numbers. It need not relate to the song.

Do you know your shapes? (AT4/2) Discuss the differences between squares and rectangles and the different shapes of the triangles.

Which way to the stable?

❑ Ask the children to devise their own mazes.

Santa's day (AT2/2) Alter the times according to the abilities of the children. Alternatively, use digital times.

❑ Make comparisons with the children's own times for various activities throughout the day.

Dot-to-dot 1 (AT2/2) Stress the importance of joining up the dots in the correct order. Calculators may be used to check answers.

How many left? (AT2/2) It may be necessary for some children to use counters.

Buying Christmas treats (AT2/2) Using plastic coins may help here.

❑ Ask the children how much change there would be from 20p. Set up a Christmas shop in the classroom.

Gift survey (AT5/3)

❑ Represent this information as a line graph or pie chart. Conducting a 'real' survey will make the exercise more meaningful.

Make a star (AT4/3)

❑ Follow up this activity with tangrams.The children may like to draw their own Christmas shapes, cut them into sections and then ask each other to put them back together.

Christmas lights (AT3/3) Each child will need several sheets to find out the total number of combinations.The same three colours should be used to make comparisons of results easier.

Measuring up for Christmas (AT2/3)

❑ The results would make a very useful basis for a data-handling computer program such as GRASS or could be made into a graph. Compare metric measurements with imperial ones. Ask the children why they think the system has changed – has it changed over completely?

Find the way Solution:

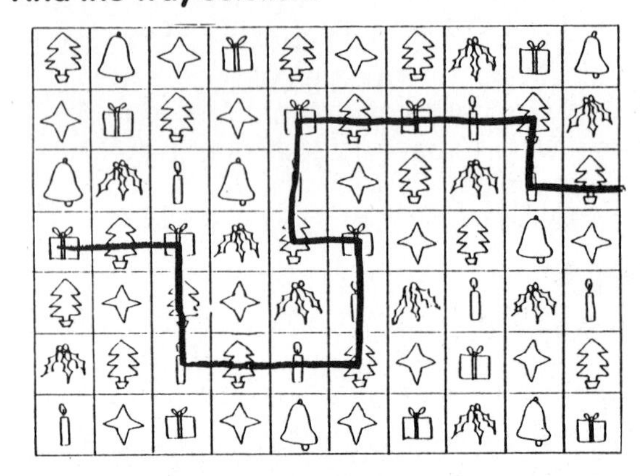

Decoration fractions (AT2/3)

❑ Photocopy these shapes on to card and cut out to make decorations or puzzles.

Snowman crossword puzzle (AT2/3)

❑ Ask the children to design their own maths

crossword puzzles. Do they work out?

Christmas toy sale (AT2/3; AT3/3)

❑ Ask the children to design their own 'machines', involving a variety of processes such as addition, multiplication, division, percentages and fractions.

Christmas coordinates (AT3/4) It is important that the coordinates are joined up in the correct order and that the dot is placed on the line, not in the square.

❑ Ask children to make up their own designs. Ask them to draw the shape first and then work out the appropriate coordinates.

Carol calculations (AT2/4) Encourage the use of calculators to check the answers.

Christmas sale (AT2/4) It may be necessary to use a calculator with this sheet.

❑ Devise follow-up activity sheets using newspaper advertisements.

Dot-to-dot 2 (AT2/4) Ensure the children work out the problems first.

❑ Ask the children to design dot-to-dots themselves.

Christmas shopping (AT2/4) Use calculators to check the answers.

❑ Cut out advertisements from newspapers to make additional activity sheets.

Science

Push or pull? (AT4/2) Have available toys similar to those depicted. Allow time for the children to explore how the various objects move. Sort the objects into groups.

❑ Ask the children to design and make their own toys that are pushed or pulled.

Christmas I-spy (AT1) This activity helps develop observation and recording skills. Children should take home their sheet and use it over the Christmas holiday.

❑ Ask the children to devise their own sheet of school objects with a Christmas/winter theme.

Investigating materials (AT1; AT3/ 1&2) Provide the actual objects for the children to handle and observe. It is important that they realise that there is not always one correct answer, and that each item can be made from different materials. Ask them to find differences and similarities between the materials and, if appropriate, ask them where the materials originally came from.

Footprints in the snow (AT1, AT2) Before referring to books, discuss what the children think the prints might be, giving their reasons.

❑ If it snows, take the children outside to look for tracks and to look at their own prints. Is it possible to tell from its prints the size, speed and direction of an animal?

Safety at Christmas (AT2; AT3) Let the children compare answers and note any differences of opinion.

❑ Make up a set of safety rules for the classroom or the school.

Movement (AT1) This activity combines work in English and science. As far as possible, allow the children to try out the movements, such as opening doors and windows. Discuss the different words that the children use to describe the movement.

❑ Develop other experiments involving movement, such as pushing and pulling, levers, pulleys and motors (AT4).

Christmas music (AT4/2&3) If possible, let the children have first hand experience of these instruments. Some instruments, such as the tambourine, may involve more than one action. Discuss the various possibilities.

Paper chains (AT1; AT3/3) Allow the children time to examine closely the different kinds of paper using hand lenses to look for differences and similarities in type, texture and so on.

❑ Go on to study paper and paper-making.

Candles (AT1; AT3/3) Hold the candle in place with Plasticine in a sand tray and ensure that the children are at a safe distance. Encourage them to observe what is actually happening, not what they assume is happening. What part of the candle is actually burning?

❑ Discuss the concept of solids, liquids and gases, and energy transfer.

Can you help Santa's elves? (AT1; AT4/2) If any items are not available, substitutes can be made. Discuss with the children the reasons behind their predictions to find out what they already know about magnetism.

A waterproof sack for Santa (AT1; AT3/3) Using hand lenses look closely at the fabrics. Ask the children to comment on differences and similarities. Discuss the concept of a fair test. Encourage the children to consider whether the pieces of fabric need to be the same size, whether they should use the same number of water drops and so on.

❑ Test coats for waterproofness and discuss how clothes protect us.

What object is that? (AT2/4) Practise using similar identification keys with real objects first. Group together objects with common characteristics, then ask the children if any of the objects belong in two or more groups.

Holly observations (AT1) Provide the children with hand lenses for this activity.

❑ Compare the holly leaves with other ever-greens found at this time of year.

Christmas lights (AT1; AT3/3) Firstly, remind the children that the electricity from batteries is safe to handle but mains electricity is *very* dangerous. It is important for the children to look closely at the diagrams to see where the wires are

touching. Circuits 2 and 4 will light up. Discuss with the children their reasons for their predictions.When the children draw their circuits discuss strength and direction of flow. (The strength of the flow remains the same all around the circuit, and the flow is circular.) Let the children look closely at a light bulb to see how it might work.
Santa's annual check-up (AT1; AT2/3) Practise with the class how to find and measure the pulse. The children can work in pairs and the teacher can act as time-keeper.
❏ Discuss other body parts and functions.

Geography

Christmas toys (AT1/1&2) This activity illustrates the first stage in making plans by identifying the outlines of objects.
❏ Draw outlines of familiar classroom objects, then ask the children to identify them.
Following directions (AT1/1&2) Read the instructions out to the class first.
❏ Reinforce directions by using games involving words such as above, below, right and left.
Mystery Christmas objects (AT1/2&3) This activity introduces the concept of a plan view, looking down at objects from above.
As Santa sees it! (AT1/3) This is an extension of the Mystery Christmas objects activity on page 78. Practise observing objects from above first.
❏ Ask the children to draw a plan view of the classroom and to test each other on object recognition.
Christmas around the world (AT2/2&3) Provide reference books about Christmas customs. Discuss the clues the children used to identify each country.
❏ Ask the children to find each country on a map. Discuss why the climate is different in each country at the same time of year.
Santa's last stop (AT1/2)
❏ Ask the children to make a map of the school and to give directions to various places within the school boundary. Extend this to a map of local streets. Reinforce the concept of left and right in PE.
Help Santa's elves tidy up (AT1/3) When using coordinates, emphasise that the positions are located by going along the base first (letters), then up the columns (numbers).
❏ Make a map of the classroom and mark in the coordinates of specific pieces of equipment and furniture.
Christmas island (AT1/4) Each journey should be measured in straight lines between the dots marked on the map.
Christmas post (AT1/4) The children will need an atlas for this activity.
❏ Ask the children to find out about Christmas posting dates for different countries, then let them work out the time it takes letters to arrive.
❏ Ask the children to choose a country and then write letters to each other, describing the weather, landscape and Christmas customs in that place.
Parcels for Christmas (AT1/4) This relates well to the previous activity, Christmas post.
❏ Ask the children to find out how much it would cost to send a parcel of a certain weight to each of these countries.
Map of Palestine (AT1/4) Show the children how to measure the coastline by using thread to follow the contour, then straightening it along a ruler to measure the distance according to the scale.
❏ Look at old maps of the Bible lands and compare them to today's maps. Which place names have changed? How have the borders of countries changed? Why could this be?
Santa's visit to Smithton (AT1/4) Ask the children to compare answers to see how many different ways have been found to give directions to the one place. What sort of vocabulary is used? What is the shortest, most direct route?
Around the world with Santa (AT1/4; AT2/5) This activity will provide practice in using an atlas and locating places.
❏ Discuss what the differences might be in each of these countries at Christmas time. Include differences in weather, clothing worn, time differences and languages.
The weather on Christmas Day (AT1/4)
❏ Study weather maps in newspapers. Discuss differences in climate in the European countries. Draw a summer weather map.

History

Baby beds (AT1/2) Find pictures of children's beds from different periods of history. Discuss the meaning of the words 'manger' and 'crib'.
❏ Let the children make model beds, considering problems such as strength, comfort, shape, available materials.
The birth of Jesus (AT1/2) This activity provides practice in sequencing. Tell the story of the birth of Jesus first if necessary.
❏ Ask the children to write about each picture and then to make a little book of the story.
Old or new? (AT1/2) Support this activity with some old and new toys. Discuss the children's reasons for determining why things are old or new.
❏ Ask the children to consider how old is old.Compare the answers of children from different age groups.
Biblical clothing (AT1/2&3)
❏ Make a study of clothing worn around the

world or compare the clothing types worn in Britain, especially by different ethnic groups.

A Christmas time-line (AT1/2&3) This activity helps to develop an understanding of chronological order.

❑ Place a large time-line around the room with further Christmas customs and events and their dates added to this list.

Fact or opinion? (AT2/3) Discuss the difference between 'fact' and 'opinion'. Are all historical writings 'true'?

❑ Look at several different accounts of the same event to demonstrate that history is often based on someone's point of view.

The history of Christmas (AT1/3) Provide the children with reference books for this activity. Solution: Across – 1. yule, 5. Nazareth, 8. Herod, 9. crackers, 10. wassail, 11. Silent Night. Down – 2. Gabriel, 3. card, 4. Bethlehem, 6. Handel, 7. Puritans.

❑ Ask the children to make up their own Christmas crosswords.

Christmas in my grandparents' day (AT3/3)

❑ Encourage the children to ask their parents the same questions and then to complete the questionnaire themselves to make comparisons between the different generations. The results could be shown on a graph or input on a computer database program.

Christmas cards (AT3/3) What deductions can be made about the period by looking at early cards? If possible, provide several examples of early cards, and compare these with a collection of modern cards.

Christmas party dressing (AT3/3) Provide reference books about costume through the ages. Dress periods from left to right: Medieval, Elizabethan, Eighteenth Century, Victorian, Edwardian, 1920s, 1990s.

❑ Ask the children to write about the clothes worn in each period and give reasons why they would or would not like to wear them.

Christmas in the past (AT3/3) The people in this illustration are making a Christmas pudding.

Christmas research (AT3/3&4) Provide reference books about Christmas, including the Bible.

Christmas customs (AT3/3) Provide reference books about Christmas customs.

❑ The questions and answers could be written on cards to make a matching game.

The Christmas story (AT1/3)

❑ This extract would be a useful reading for Christmas performances, it is taken from the *Good News (Today's Version) Bible.*

Technology

Gift tags (AT2/2&3) Provide some real gift tags for the children to look at. Discuss the importance of clear labelling, use of colours, Christmas themes and so on.

Christmas stamps (AT1/3; AT2/3; AT4/ 2&3) Provide samples of Christmas and other commemorative stamps and first day covers for the children to look at. Explain what is meant by a first day cover.

❑ Compare stamps from different countries. Ask the children to find out about the history of stamps.

Christmas advertising (AT2/3) Look at advertisements in magazines and newspapers to provide a stimulus for ideas. This activity could be used with New Christmas toy on page 107.

❑ Let the children make large advertising posters for the classroom wall.

New Christmas toy! (AT1/3; AT2 2&3; AT3/2&3) Have a collection of toys in the classroom. The survey is an important part of this activity as it identifies a need and provides the stimulus for the design. Display the survey results as a graph.

❑ Ask the children to evaluate their toys. What improvements could they make? Extend the activity into science work on how toys work. Introduce concepts of energy, levers and motion.

Plan a Christmas party (AT1/3; AT3/3) Organise a group discussion to help the children decide what needs to be done or purchased. Compare results to see if anything has been omitted. Which party appears to be the best organised? Why is this?

Christmas cake recipe (AT1/2&3) This activity provides practice in sequencing and planning.

❑ Help the children to bake and decorate a Christmas cake.

Designing Christmas decorations (AT2/2&3) Each child may require several sheets. Encourage them to find out how many different designs are possible. The finished shapes could be stuck on to card and hung up.

Party invitations (AT2/2&3) Provide a collection of real party invitations to give the children some ideas for their own designs.

❑ Use the designs to make invitations to a class party.

Make a postal van (AT2/2&3; AT3/3; AT4/3) Read a *Postman Pat* story or Janet and Allan Ahlberg's *The Jolly Postman* as a stimulus for this activity.

Toy-making machine (AT2/3) This activity allows the children the opportunity to design according to a set of needs.

❑ Ask the children to make models of their toy-making machines.

A new sleigh for Santa (AT2/3) This activity also provides the opportunity to design according to a set of needs or criteria. Evaluate the designs on the basis of whether they are successful in

meeting these needs.
❑ Let the children make models of the sleighs.

Craft

Advent calendar 1 & 2 This will be more durable if photocopied on to thin white card. Explain the importance of colouring in the pictures before cutting out the windows.
❑ The children may want to design their own calendars once they understand how they are made. They could stick match boxes behind the windows so that small gifts/sweets could be placed inside them.
Make a pop-up Christmas card This design should be enlarged on a photocopier.
❑ This simple method of making a pop-up section could be incorporated into the children's own card designs.
Make a stained-glass window
This page can be successfully photocopied straight on to thin black card. Explain that no adhesive tape should overlap as this will show up when hung up in the light.
Make a lantern This pattern will work with paper or thin card. Pictures can also be added to the reverse side of the lantern so that both the outside and inside are decorated
❑ Invite the children to decorate their lanterns with glitter, beads, ribbon and so on.
Christmas bookmarks
❑ These bookmarks may inspire the children to try their own designs and can be a good starting point for discussing possible shapes, lengths, patterns and so on.
Make a basket This basket works successfully on paper or thin card.
Make a Santa mobile The body parts can be enlarged on a photocopier.
❑ Encourage the children to design their own mobiles, incorporating moving parts and textured surfaces.
Making decorations This activity is simple but effective. Once the children each have one template of the diamond, they can trace and make many more.
❑ The designs could be mounted on backing card as a group or hung separately as tree decorations.
Make a nativity scene 1, 2 & 3
❑ Let the children make a stable from a cardboard box, painted or covered with coloured paper and lined with straw with a large star at the top.
Christmas alphabet Suggest that the designs may also be centred around a winter theme if children run out of ideas.
❑ The letters could be enlarged to make a mural. The design would also be suitable for embroidery or collage.
Christmas wrapping
❑ Instead of copying the design, let the children rotate or reflect the pattern to create a different effect. Alternatively, let them design their own shapes in each square. Use gold and silver felt-tipped pens or glitter to add sparkle.

General

This section contains large, outline drawings of Christmas subjects. They are not intended to be used merely as templates, but as a stimulus for a wide range of creative activities.

The following ideas may prove useful in the classroom.

- The shapes could be enlarged, traced on to overhead projector acetate sheets and projected on to a wall.
- A stained-glass window effect could be made by tracing enlarged shapes on to black paper, cutting out sections and then sticking coloured acetate film behind the spaces. The Father Christmas, star and candle shapes are particularly suited to this.
- The shapes could be traced on to card to make mobiles or free-standing displays.
- The pages could be used for discussion purposes. For example, the nativity scene could be used to illustrate the costumes of the time, the people involved and so on.
- The pages can be used to stimulate ideas for the children's own designs.
- Some of the designs are suitable for use as patterns for craft activities. For example, the stocking could be used as a paper pattern to make a sewn stocking.
- Alternatively you may decide to use the shapes as a basis for the production of your own worksheets.

Name ____________________

✤ Write Santa a letter. Tell him about the things you do at Christmas. Ask him what he does at Christmas.

Name ________________

Rudolph's Christmas

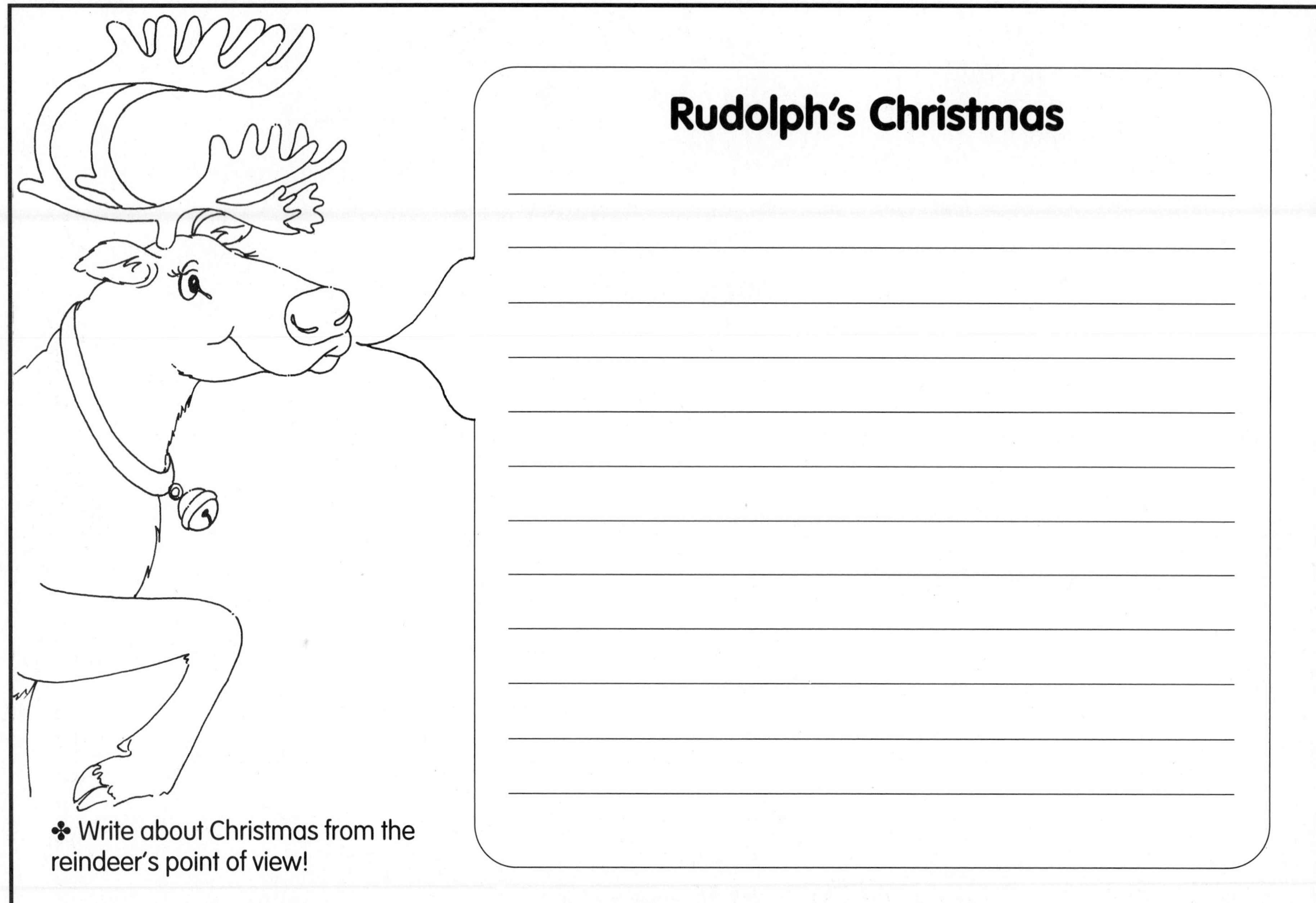

✤ Write about Christmas from the reindeer's point of view!

Name ____________________

Christmas writing paper

Name ____________

Christmas storyboard

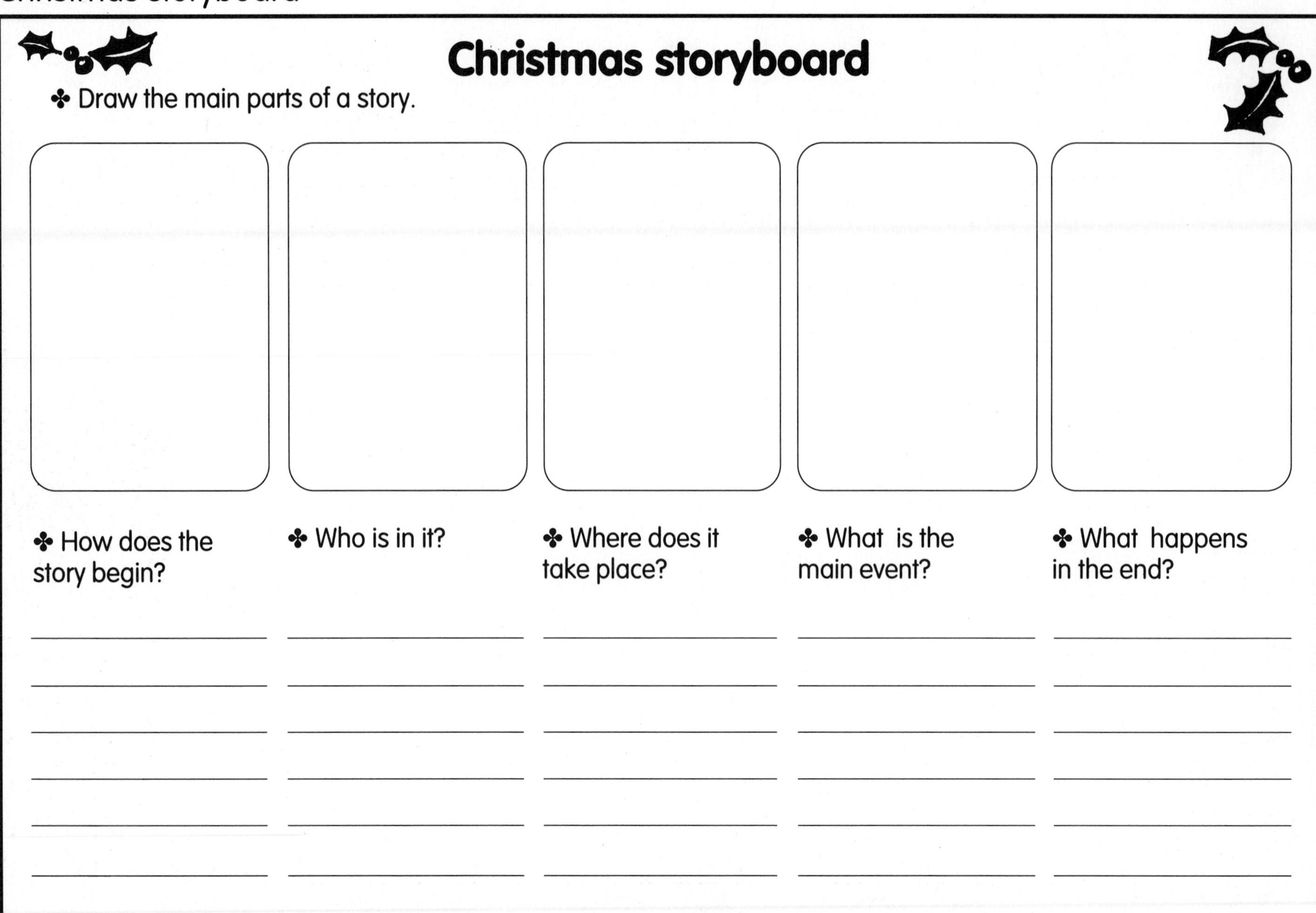

Christmas storyboard

✤ Draw the main parts of a story.

✤ How does the story begin?

✤ Who is in it?

✤ Where does it take place?

✤ What is the main event?

✤ What happens in the end?

Name ____________________

✤ Write about Christmas in your house.

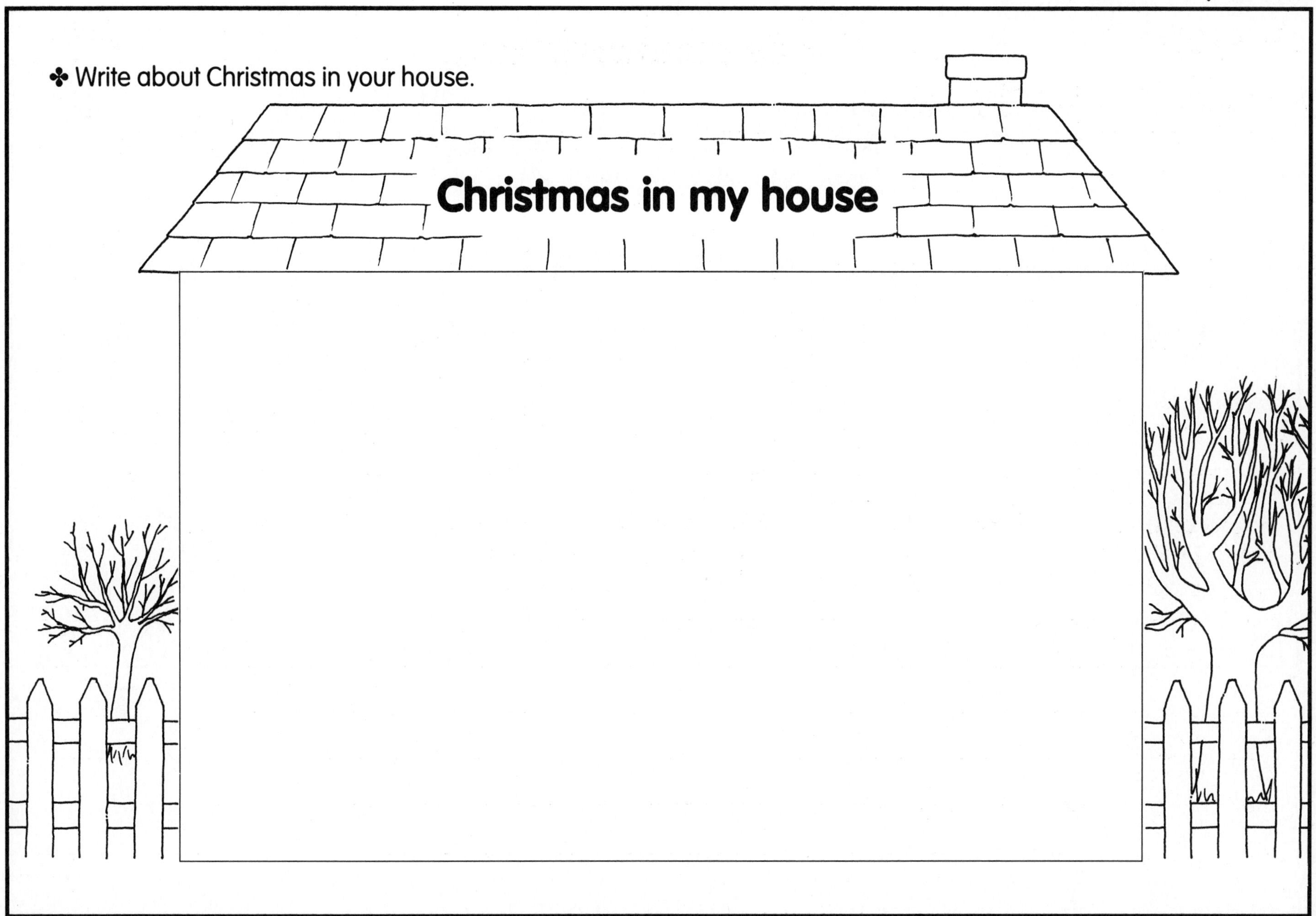

Name ____________

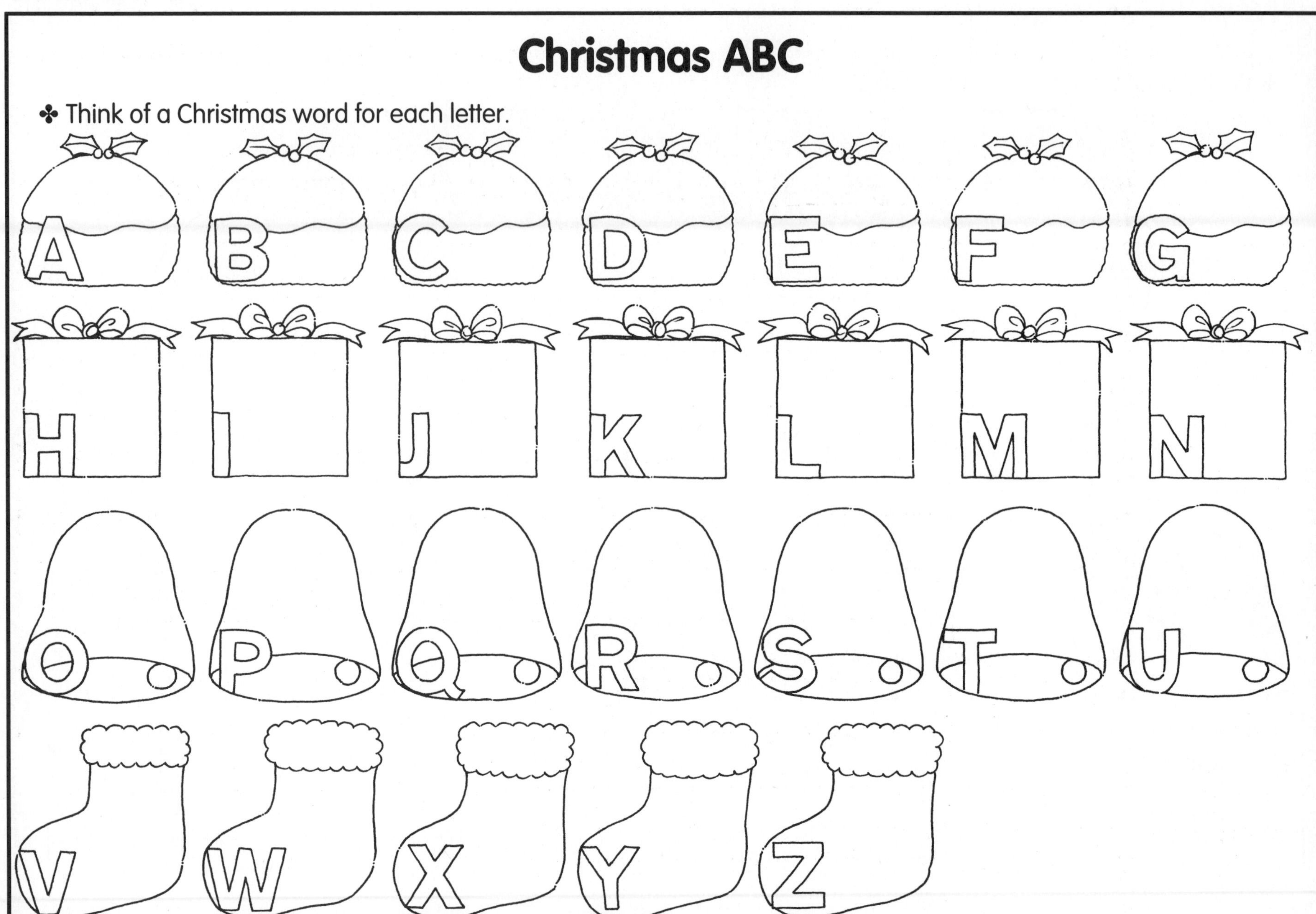
Christmas ABC
✤ Think of a Christmas word for each letter.
A
B
C
D
E
F
G
H
I
J
K
L
M
N
O
P
Q
R
S
T
U
V
W
X
Y
Z

Name ____________________

✤ Write about the best Christmas you have had. Use the word bank below to help you.

word bank

present	early
morning	gift
Santa	surprise
wrapping	bows
lights	candle
reindeer	crackers
table	turkey
tinsel	balloons
cake	tree
aunt	uncle
cousin	friend
mother	father
brother	sister
Christmas	
decorations	
plum pudding	

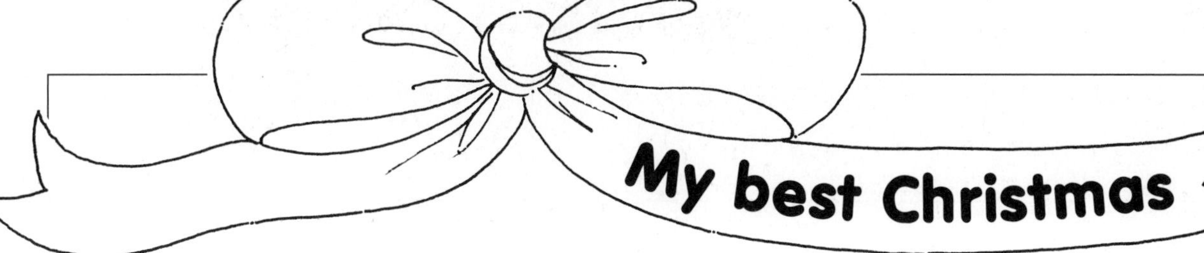

____

____

____

____

____

____

____

____

____

____

____

Name ______________

Christmas carol puzzle

Christmas carol puzzle

✤ Write the first letter of each object in its box. The letters will form the name of a Christmas carol.

✤ Write the name of the carol here:

Name ____________________

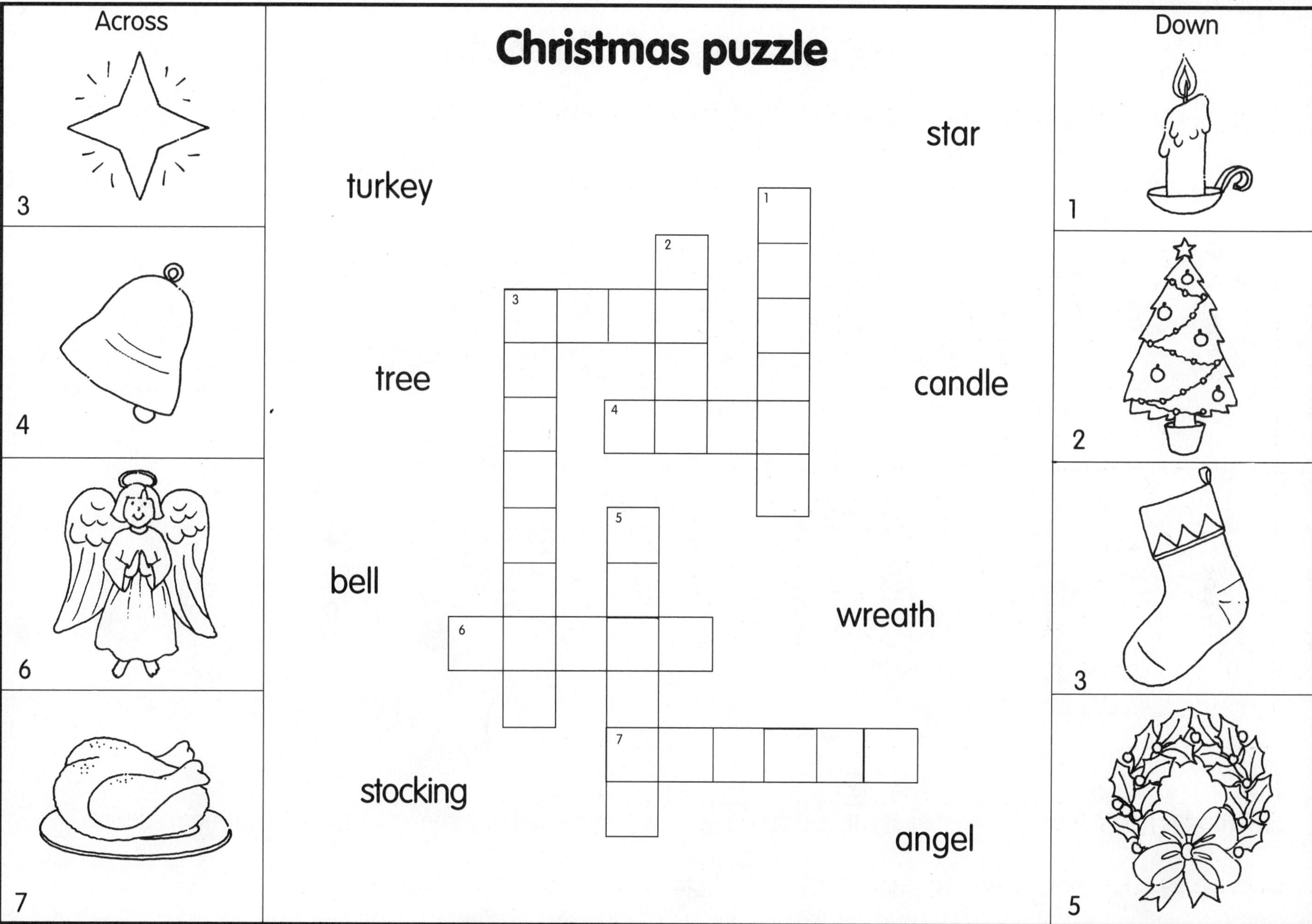
Across
Christmas puzzle
Down
3
4
6
7
1
2
3
5
star
turkey
tree
candle
bell
wreath
stocking
angel

Name ______________

The sounds of Christmas

Here are some familiar sounds we hear at Christmas time.

✤ Describe the sounds of these Christmas things:

The __________ of unwrapping presents.

The __________ of snow underfoot.

The __________ of surprised children.

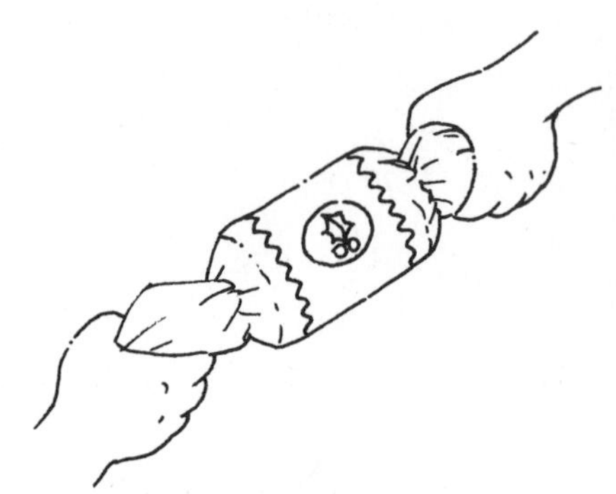

The __________ of Christmas crackers.

✤ Think of some more Christmas sounds. Draw the objects and describe the sounds.

Christmas acrostics

Acrostics are poems where the first letter of each line spells a word when read downwards, like this:

P eter adores Christmas. He
L oves to
U nwrap all his stocking gifts before
M um and dad are fully awake. But

P eter loves the presents
U nder the sparkling tree best. He
D oesn't know what's in them so he
D ives in and grabs the largest first.
I n no time at all they're all unwrapped.
N o more surprises left. Exhausted, he
G ladly takes a rest!

✤ Make up your own acrostic for this word:

C

H

R

I

S

T

M

A

S

✤ Now make up some more of your own. Share them with your friends.

Name ____________________

How much do you know about Christmas? The story of Jesus? Our Christmas traditions? Christmas in other countries? What would you like to find out about Christmas?

✤ Write below what you know and what you would like to find out.

Shaped poems

✤ Write a poem to fit inside this tree.

A
new
star
shone out that
night to show the
kings the way to
baby
Jesus

A
Candle
is a
lovely
sight,
It helps
me see
in the
night.

✤ Write some more shaped Christmas poems of your own.

Name ____________

Match the crackers

✤ Match up each half of the crackers by colouring the word and its meaning in the same colour.

Christmas words

These Christmas words have been written to look like their meaning:

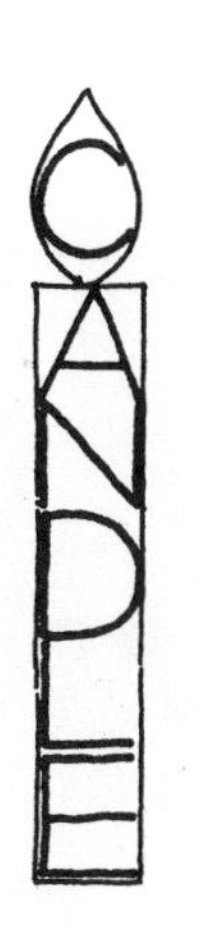

✤ Make up some more of your own. Draw them here.

'S' word crossword

Name ____________

'S' word crossword

The answers to this Christmas puzzle all begin with the letter 's'.

Across

2. The Kings followed this to find baby Jesus.

5. Jesus was born in a _ _ _ _ _ _

6. We _ _ _ _ carols at Christmas.

7. Mary and Joseph found _ _ _ _ _ _ _ in the stable.

Down

1. Another name for Father Christmas.

3. A present we don't know about is a _ _ _ _ _ _ _

4. Santa rides on this.

5. Wrapping up presents helps to get us in the Christmas _ _ _ _ _ _

Name ____________________

Christmas comic strip

- Fill in the words you think the characters are saying.
- Make up your own Christmas comic.

Name ____________

The first Christmas

✤ Tell the story of the birth of Jesus in your own words. Use the pictures to help you. Use the back of this sheet if you need more space.

Name ____________________

Find another word

✤ Find some words that have the same meanings as the words below.

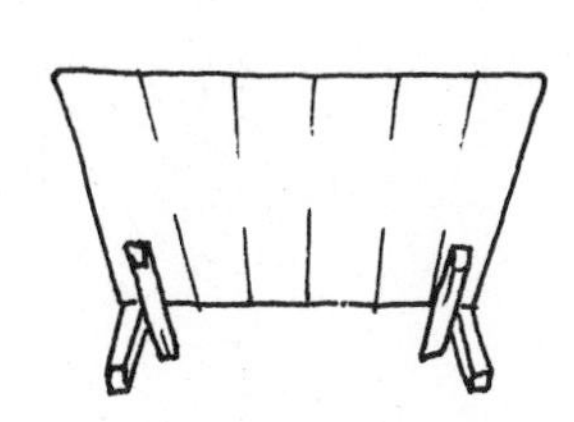

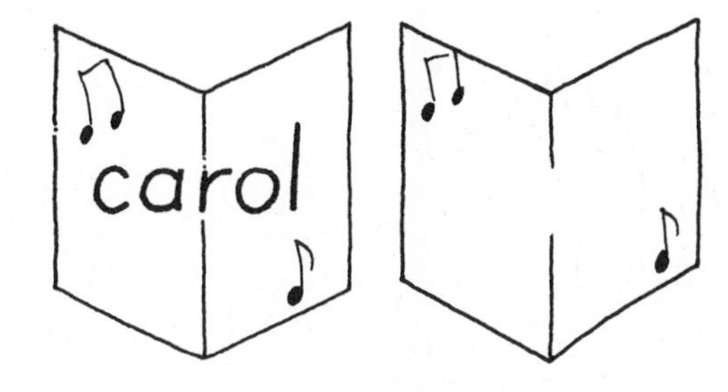

✤ Compare your answers with other people. How many different words are there?

Name ____________________

De-coding Christmas messages

De-coding Christmas messages

✤ De-code this Christmas message.

,

How R ? am
9. a toy 4
X-mas. M+ has 5
like 1?
have +n good b
y+ so hope get lots
of .
from
James.

✤ Now write your own coded Christmas letter in the space below. Ask a friend to work it out!

Christmas word fun

✤ Unscramble these Christmas words:

t s o d c e o n i a r ____________

s l h g i t ____________

n t p e e s r ____________

r e m n g a ____________

e l t s b a ____________

d h h e e s p r ____________

✤ Use these words in a sentence:

gift ____________

Jesus ____________

star ____________

tree ____________

Santa ____________

✤ How many words can you make from the letters in this greeting? (The first one is done for you.)

Merry Christmas

star

Name ____________________

Christmas word search

Christmas word search

✤ All the words in the list below can be found in this word search grid. They have been written across, down and diagonally. Circle each word as you find it. The first one has been done for you.

Word list:

carol	saviour	tree
joy	bell	holly
ivy	inn	stable
lights	yule	crib
eat	goose	star
ribbon	angel	gift
manger	baby	turkey
toys	cracker	wise men
shepherd	decorations	

c	a	r	o	l	b	e	f	e	a	l	m	o
r	e	c	i	m	i	e	l	d	d	a	b	e
a	f	l	m	v	a	u	b	e	s	t	a	r
c	e	t	t	o	y	s	m	c	e	a	b	i
k	l	u	b	y	w	e	h	o	l	l	y	b
e	a	r	m	a	n	g	e	r	b	i	e	b
r	e	k	l	e	b	y	e	a	t	g	y	o
s	h	e	p	h	e	r	d	t	e	h	t	n
t	e	y	s	e	a	w	f	i	j	t	r	l
a	b	d	e	y	r	i	g	o	o	s	e	a
b	e	l	l	m	g	e	i	n	y	a	e	n
l	s	a	v	i	o	u	r	s	e	b	n	g
e	y	m	o	p	c	r	i	b	a	i	y	e
b	e	w	i	s	e	m	e	n	y	a	b	l

The story of Christmas

A crossword puzzle

The following passage tells the story of Christmas.

✤ Work out what the words in the spaces should be and then write these words in the puzzle.

On the ______ (7 down) of ________' (14 across) birth, a bright ______ (11 across) could be seen above the _____________ (17 across) where ________ (4 across) and __________ (12 across) had rested because there was no room at the ______ (10 across). Three ______ ______ (8 across) came from the _______ (13 down) with gifts for the ____ (5 across) born _______ (3 down), the _______ (11 down) of ______ (15 down). They brought gifts of _________________ (2 down), gold and _______ (9 down) to give to the baby who was wrapped in ____________ (1 down) __________ (16 across) and lying in a __________ (6 across).

Name ____________

Christmas word puzzle

✤ Fit the following words into their proper places in the crossword grid. One has been done for you.

two-letter words:	at	on	he	be
three-letter words :	eat	boy	joy	pet
four-letter words :	sent sing	star sell	crib king	bell mail
five-letter words :	choir trees	enjoy	angel	
six-letter words :	ribbon	turkey		
eight-letter words :	stocking nativity	presents		
nine-letter word :	Christmas			

A Christmas tale

✤ Read the story and fill in the gaps.

Late one Christmas __________ Katy heard a strange ________ outside the door. She _________ through the curtains to try to see ________ it was. A man was ____________ there. He _______ a long black coat that had patches on it. His trousers ______ worn and had holes at the knees. His _______ were peeping out of holes in his shoes.

Katy ran to tell her mother and _________ about the man. Her ________ went to the door. He spoke to the ______ . 'There's no _______ to be afraid, Katy,' he ______ . 'The man is selling kittens.' Katy looked in the _____ the man was holding. Inside she saw two __________ . One was black and white with a long fluffy ______ , and one was ginger and white with a white patch over one ____ . Katy was allowed to buy the ginger one. She was very happy.

Katy's mother invited the _____ inside for a hot drink and some cake.

✤ Draw a picture of Katy's Christmas.

Name ____________

How many?

Name ____________________

Gingerbread men

✤ How many buttons are there on these gingerbread men?

✤ Draw the correct number of buttons on these gingerbread men.

5

4

6

10

Name ____________

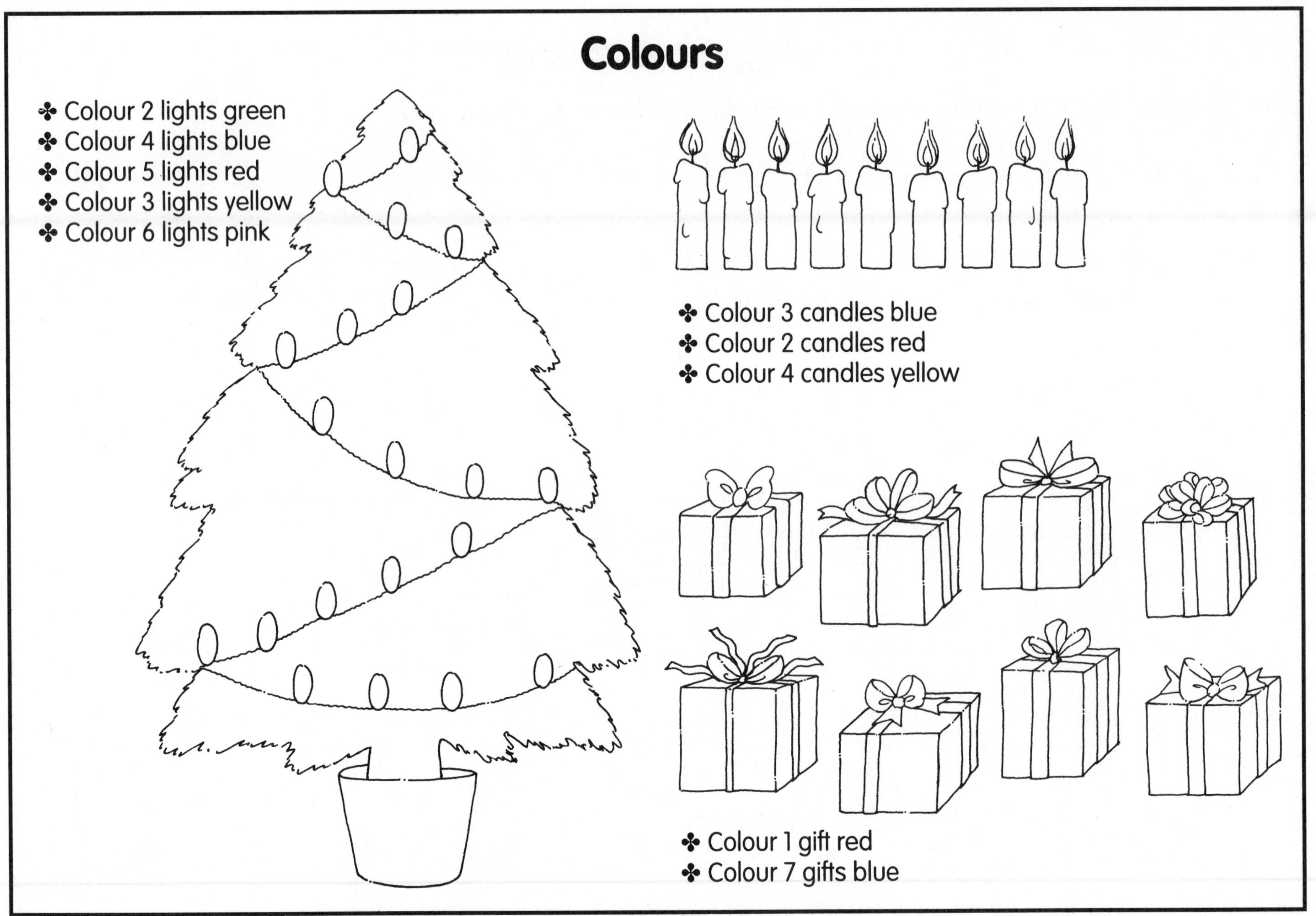
Colours
✤ Colour 2 lights green
✤ Colour 4 lights blue
✤ Colour 5 lights red
✤ Colour 3 lights yellow
✤ Colour 6 lights pink
✤ Colour 3 candles blue
✤ Colour 2 candles red
✤ Colour 4 candles yellow
✤ Colour 1 gift red
✤ Colour 7 gifts blue

Name ____________________

2 more than

✤ Draw 2 more of each of these objects. How many are there in each group now?

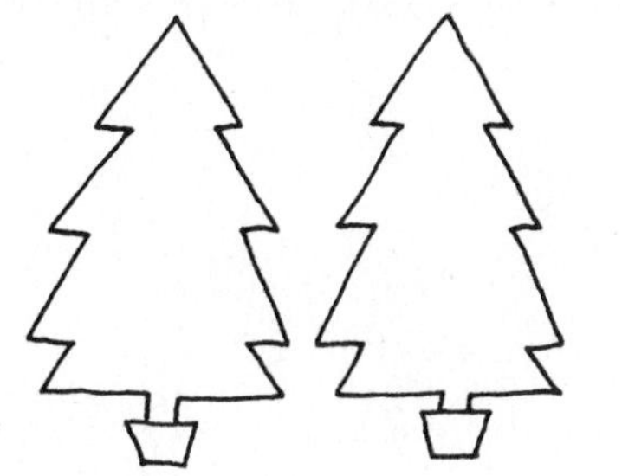

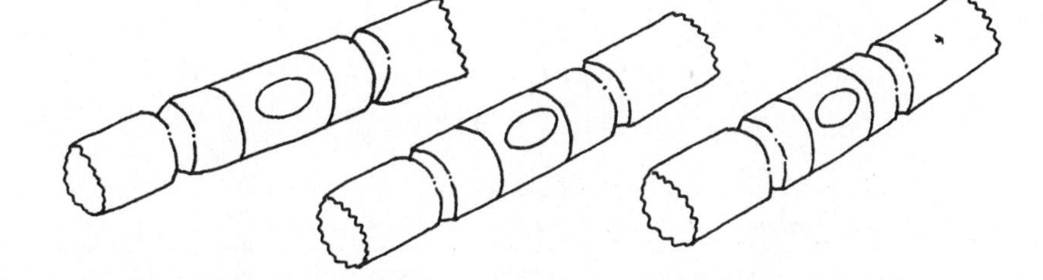

Name ______________

The twelve days of Christmas 1

✤ Draw the correct number of objects in each square to represent the gifts for each day of Christmas.

1st day	2nd day	3rd day
4th day	**5th day**	**6th day**

Name ____________________

The twelve days of Christmas 2

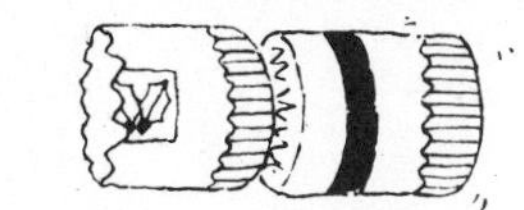

✤ Draw the correct number of objects in each square to represent the gifts for each day of Christmas.

7th day	8th day	9th day
10th day	**11th day**	**12th day**

Name ____________________

Do you know your shapes?

Do you know your shapes?

✤ Colour in this stained-glass window in these colours:

Circles – yellow

Rectangles – blue

Squares – green

Triangles – red

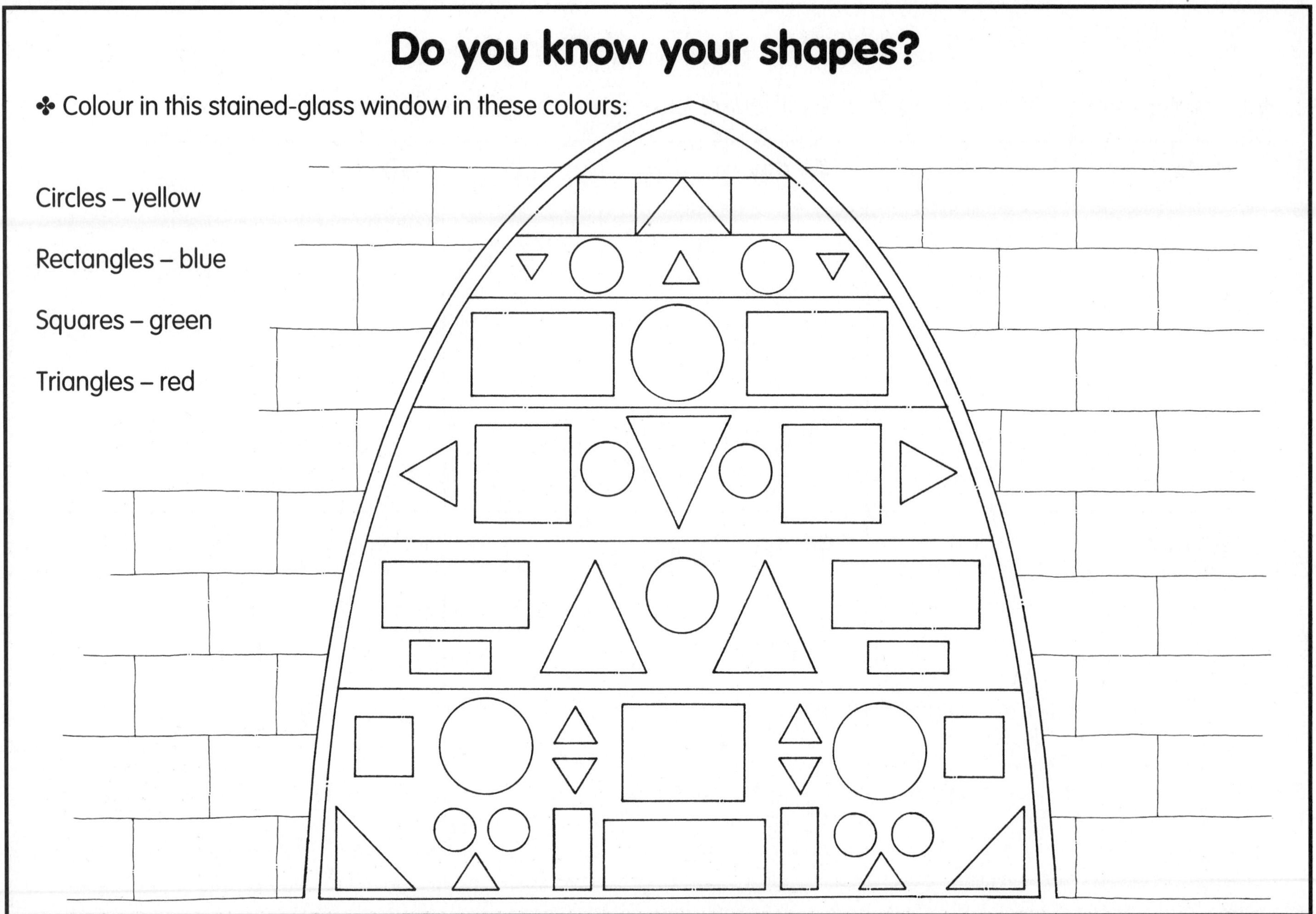

Name ____________________

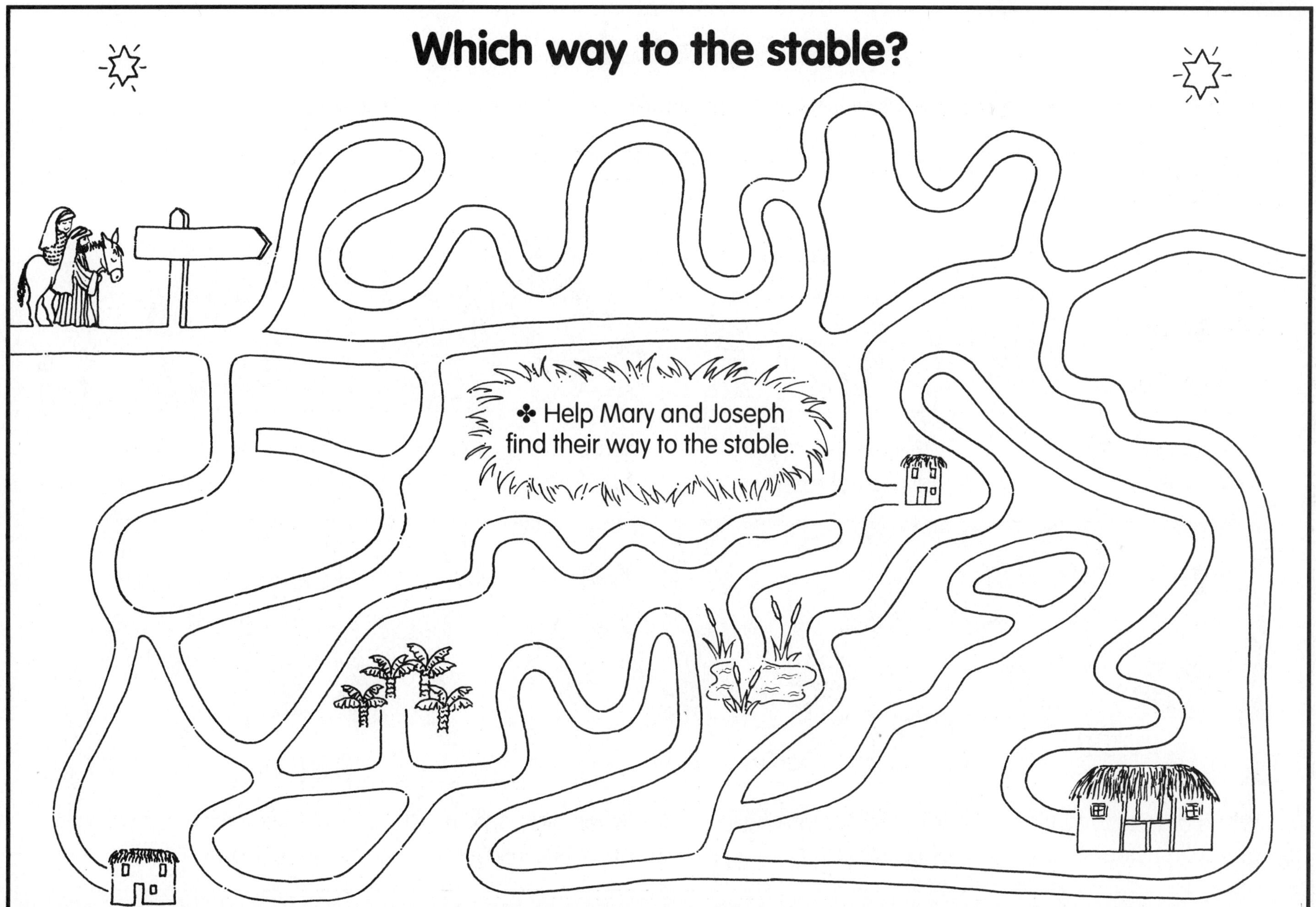
Which way to the stable?
✤ Help Mary and Joseph find their way to the stable.

Name ____________________

Santa's day

On Christmas Eve Santa has a very busy time. Write the time for each part of Santa's day.

Name ____________________

Dot-to-dot 1

✤ Work out each problem. Join answer 1 to answer 2, answer 2 to answer 3, and so on. You will end up with a Christmas picture. Finish drawing the picture and colour it in.

1) 2 + 1 =

2) 6 + 3 =

3) 4 + 2 =

4) 5 + 5 =

5) 5 + 3 =

6) 3 + 2 =

7) 2 + 0 =

8) 5 + 2 =

9) 3 + 0 =

7

6

9

Name ____________

How many left?

Each of these sacks had 10 presents inside. Father Christmas has taken some out of each one.

✤ How many are left in each sack?

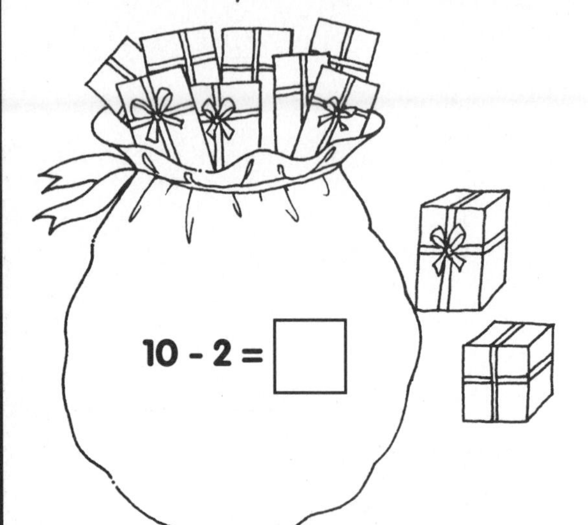

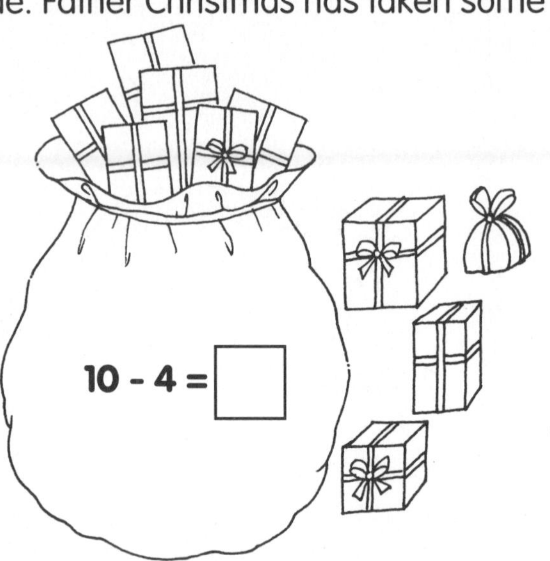

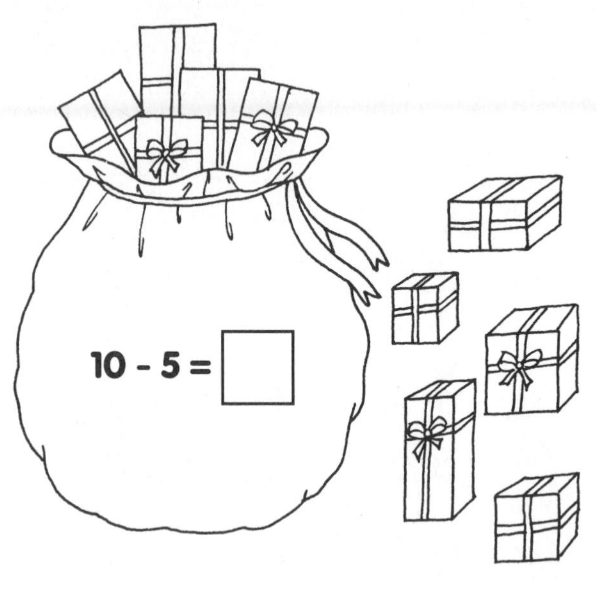

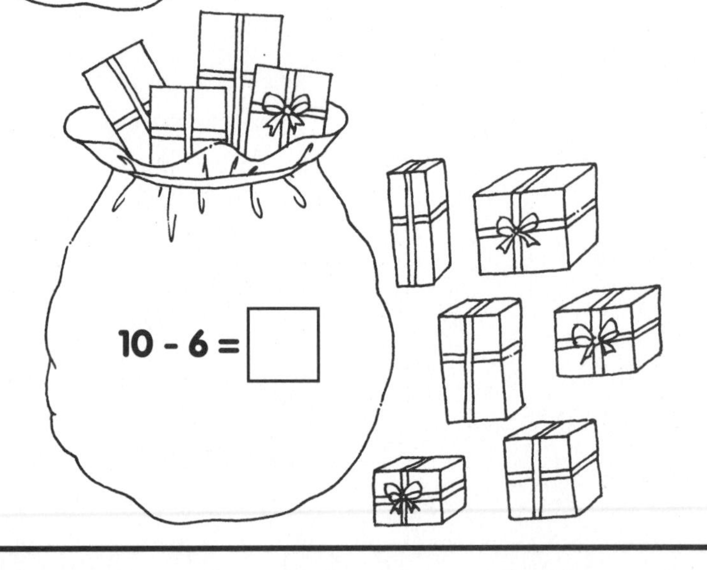

Buying Christmas treats

✤ Sam is helping his mum and dad to buy Christmas treats. How much money would he need to buy these things?

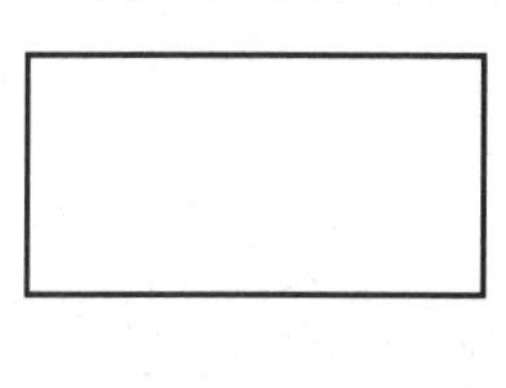

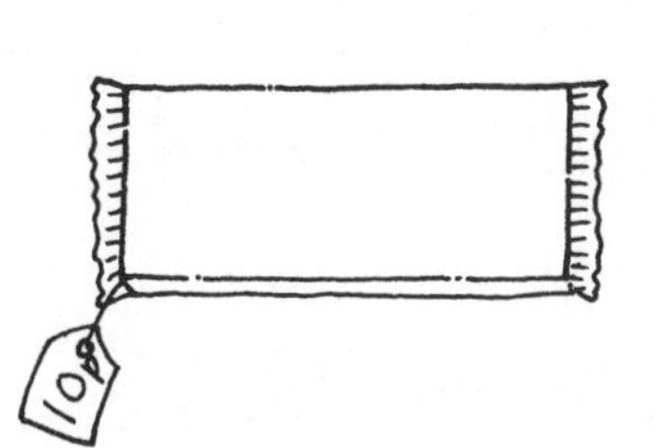

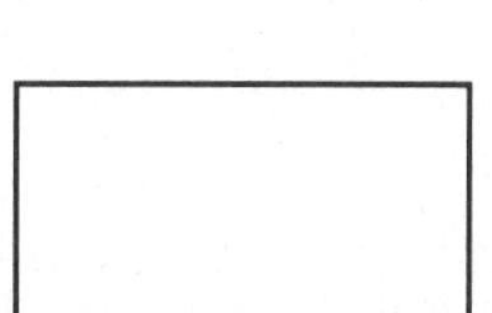

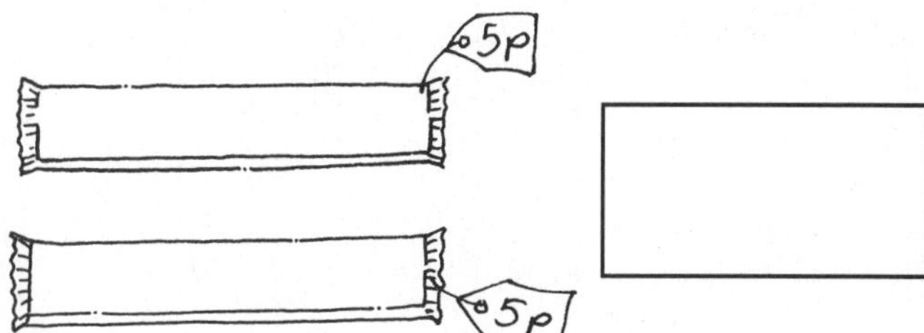

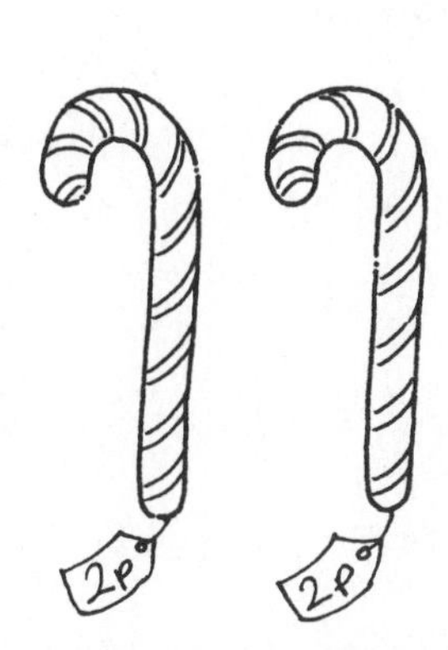

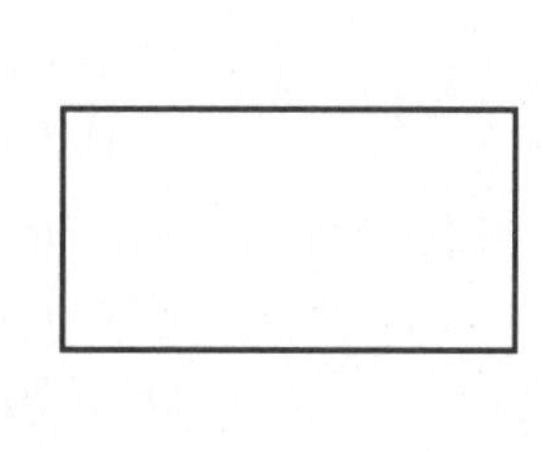

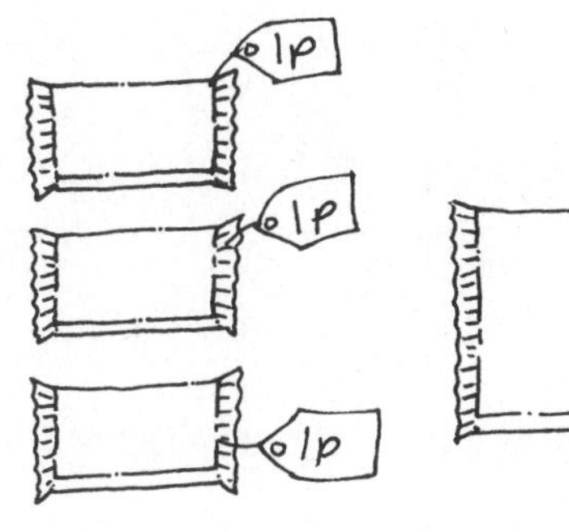

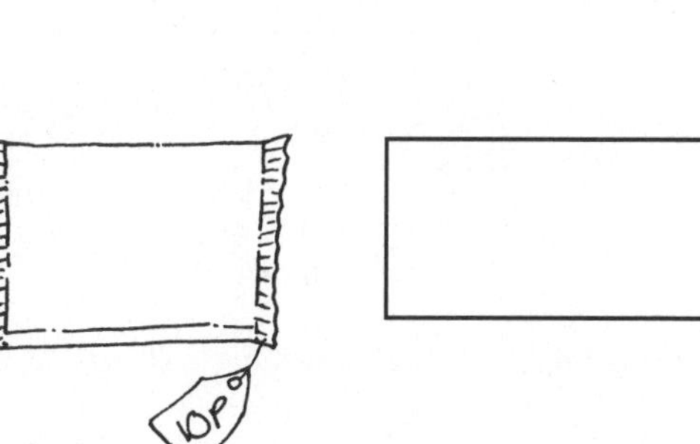

Name ____________________

Gift survey

This is a graph showing the gifts some children in one class expected to receive for Christmas.

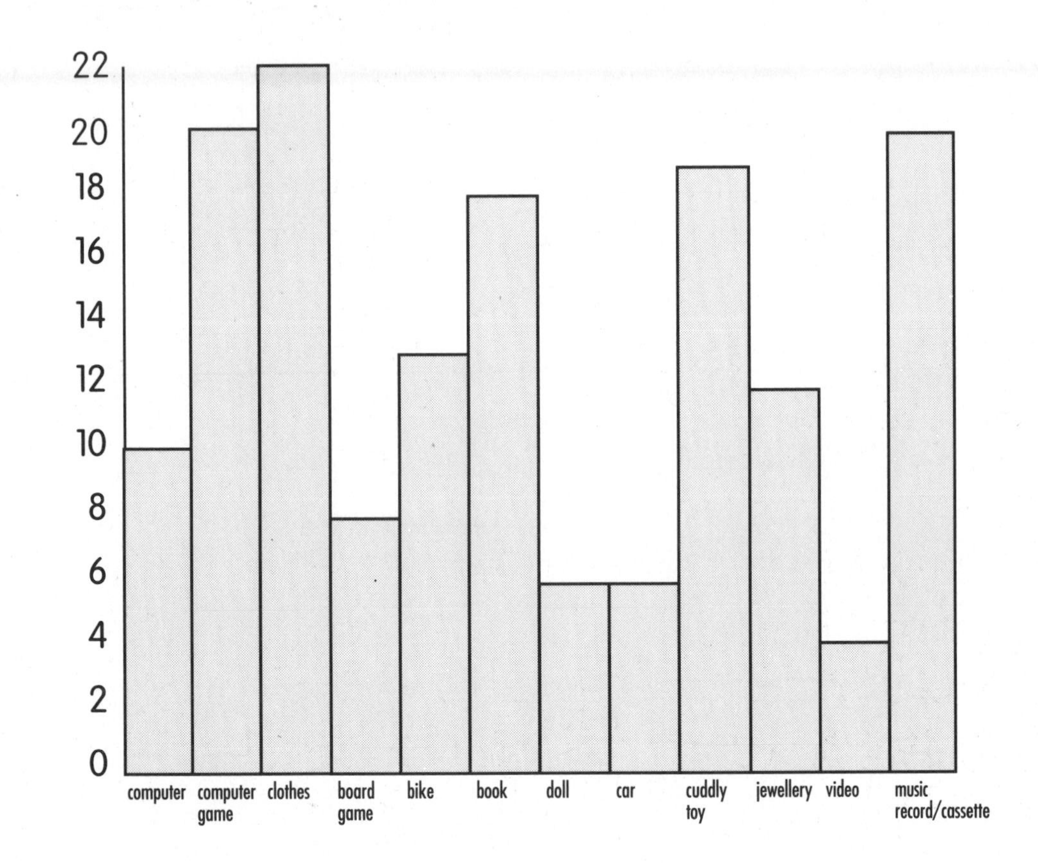

✤ Conduct a survey of your own class to see how the results compare to these.

✤ Answer the following questions by referring to the graph.

- What is the most popular gift?
- How many children expect to receive a computer game?
- Which is the least likely gift?
- How many children wanted a bike as a gift?
- How many more children wanted a book compared to a board game?
- How many children expected a cuddly toy for Christmas?
- Which gift is expected by exactly half the number of children who wanted records?
- How many children wanted jewellery for Christmas?

 Make a star 

✤ Cut out the shapes on the right and fit them into the star below. Do not overlap any pieces.

✤ Use the pieces to make another shape.

Name ____________

Christmas lights

✤ Using only 3 colours, how many different ways can you colour these sets of Christmas tree lights?

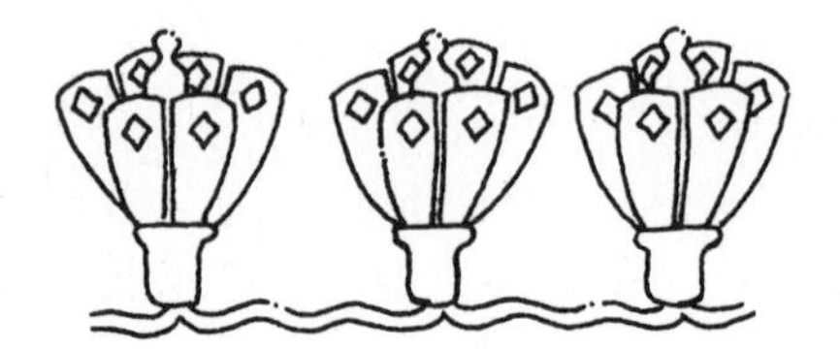

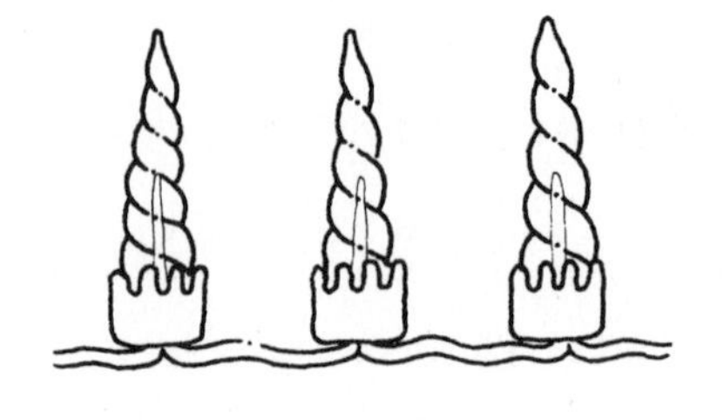

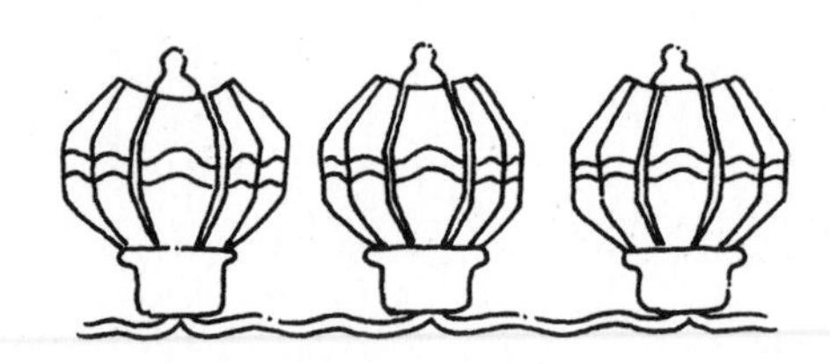

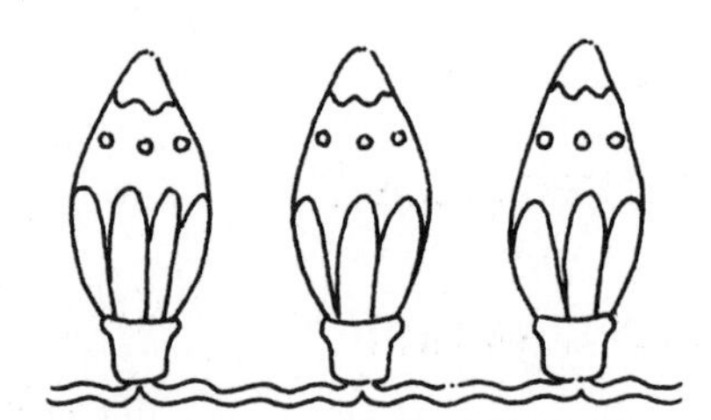

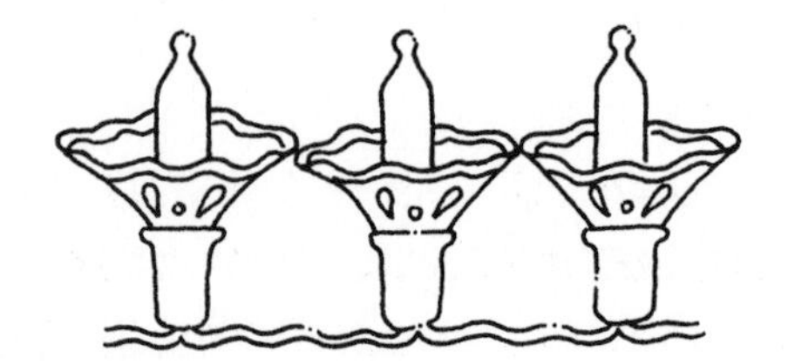

Measuring up for Christmas

When Santa gives clothes as presents, he needs to know if they are the right size!

✤ Fill in your vital statistics to make sure your clothes will be a good fit.

my height: ____________________ my weight: ____________________

head measurement: ____________________ neck measurement: ____________________

length of arm from armpit to wrist: __________________ wrist measurement: _________________

length of hand from wrist to tip of longest finger: ____________________

width of palm: ____________________ length of thumb: ____________________

length of fingers 1: ____________ 2: ____________ 3: ____________ 4: ____________

chest measurement: ____________ waist: ____________ ankle measurement: ____________

length of foot: ____________________ width of foot: ____________________

✤ Trace around your hand and your foot on squared paper.
Work out the area and perimeter of each.

✤ Compare your measurements with those of your friends.

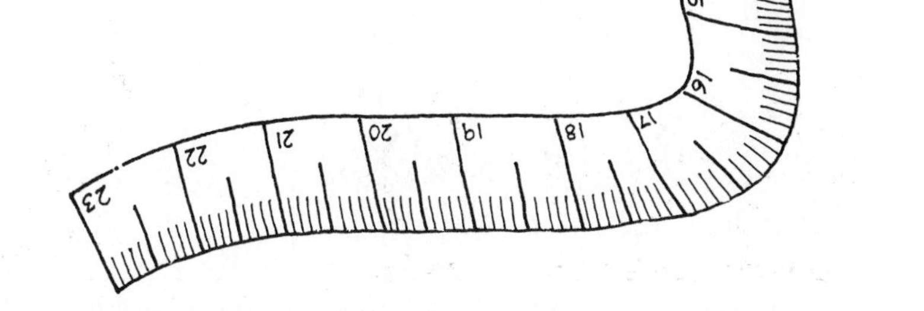

Name ____________

Find the way

✤ Find a pathway from LEFT to RIGHT that passes through only three different Christmas shapes.
You must not make any diagonal moves.

Decoration fractions

✤ Colour
2/6 red
2/6 blue
2/6 yellow

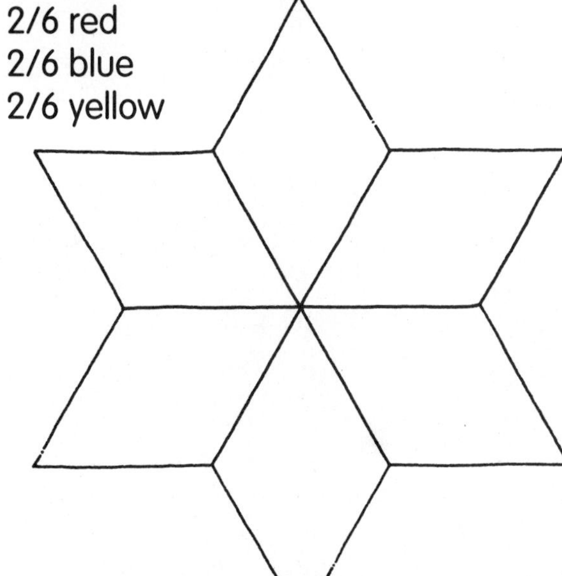

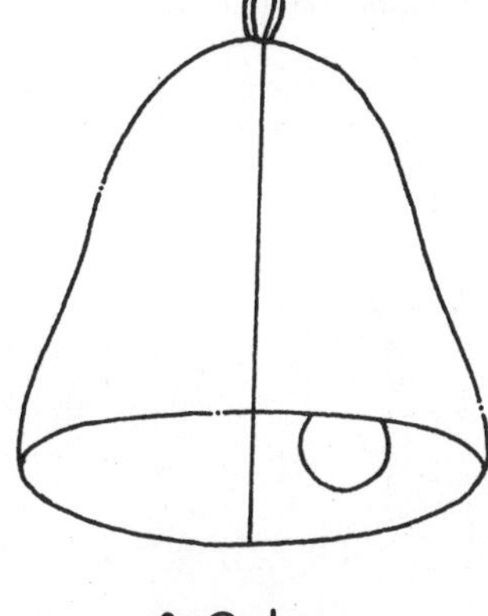

✤ Colour
1/2 red
1/2 blue

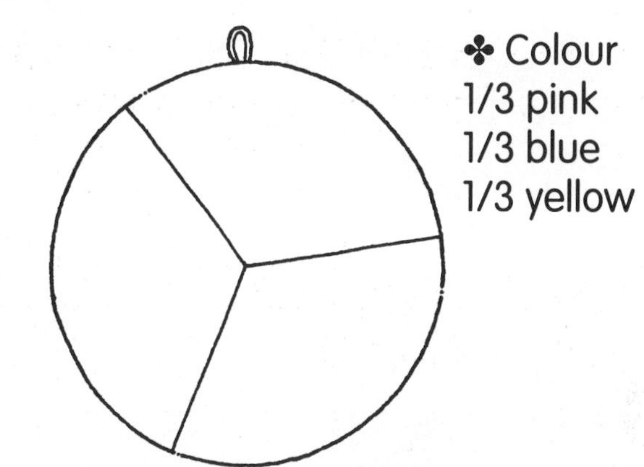

✤ Colour
1/3 pink
1/3 blue
1/3 yellow

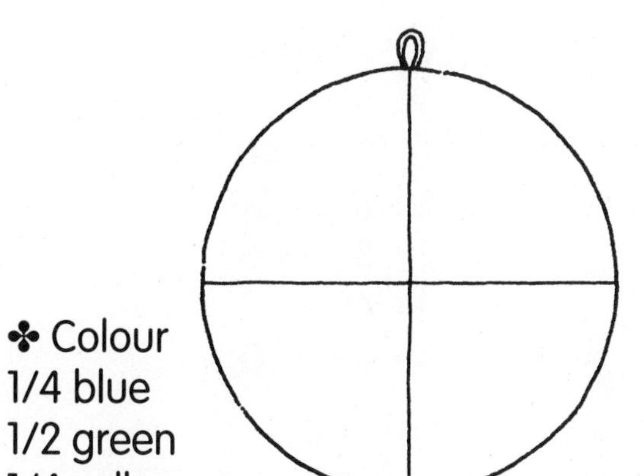

✤ Colour
1/4 blue
1/2 green
1/4 yellow

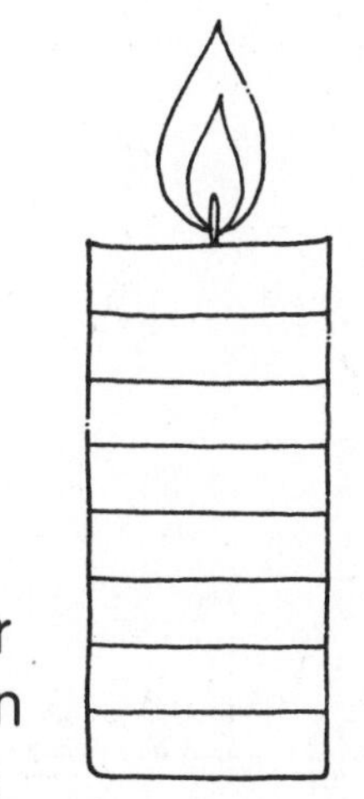

✤ Colour
1/4 green
3/4 blue

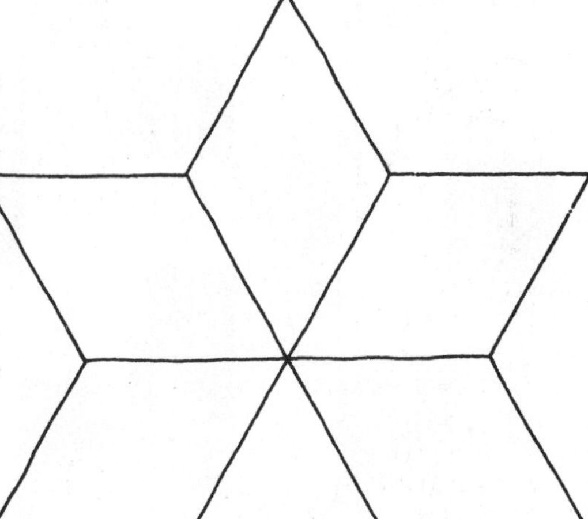

✤ Colour
1/2 red
1/2 yellow

Name ____________________

Snowman crossword puzzle

Snowman crossword puzzle

✤ Complete the crossword.
1 Across is done for you.

Across

1. 50 – 40
2. 500 + 21
4. 56 – 10
5. 910 + 13
8. 42 + 10
9. 125 + 20
11. 75 – 10
13. 10 + 18
15. 200 + 9
16. 750 – 1

Down

1. 146 + 3
2. 66 – 10
3. 20 – 5
4. 33 + 10
6. 214 – 10
7. 800 + 26
9. 92 + 40
10. 100 – 50
12. 500 + 39
14. 40 + 47
15. 49 – 20

Christmas toy sale

The local toy factory has just invented a new machine which will change all their old price tags into new price tags ready for the Christmas sales. Unfortunately, it has broken down.

✤ Look at the machine and work out what the new tags should say.

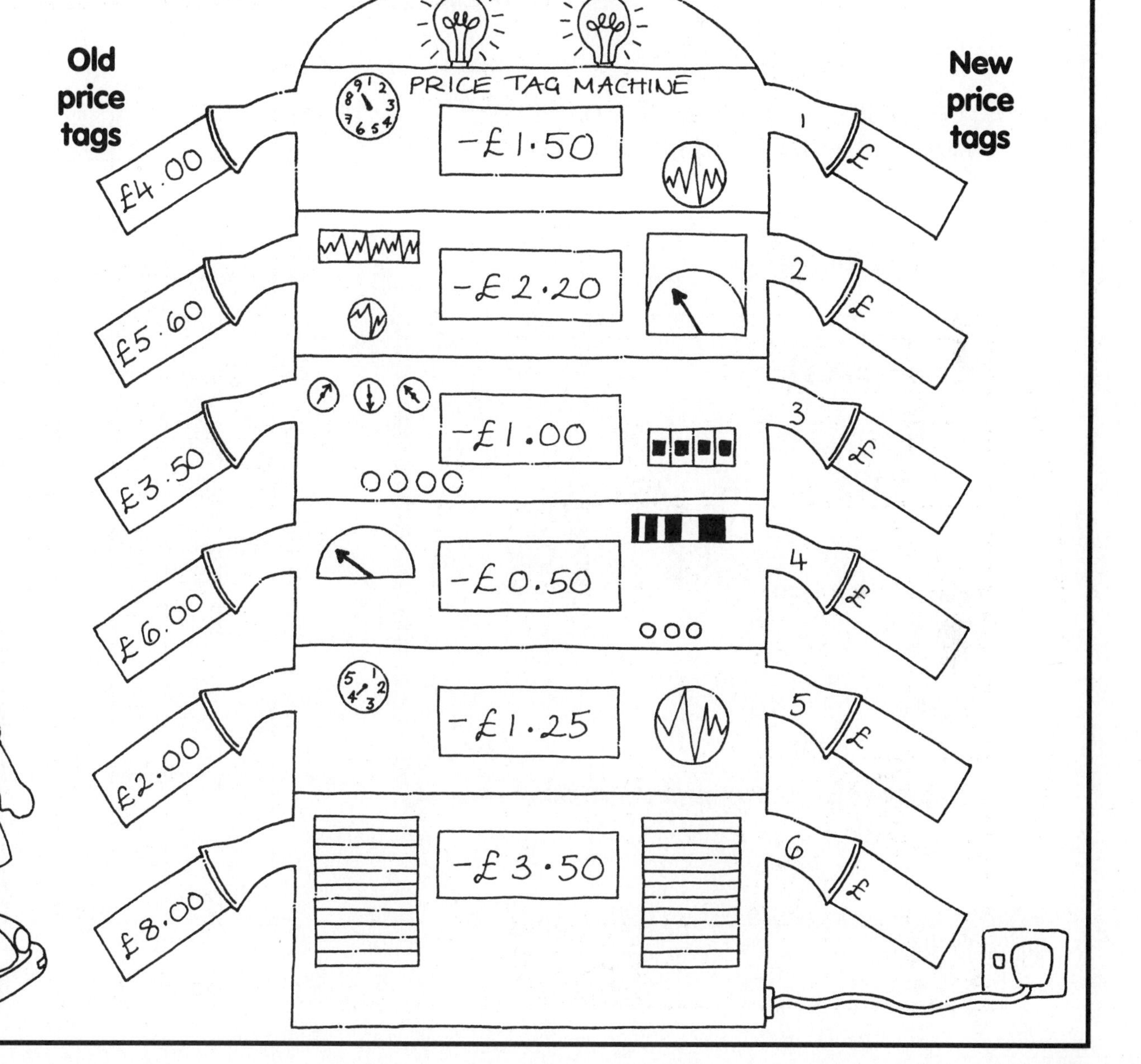

Christmas coordinates

✤ Join up these coordinates in the order they are written and you will end up with three pictures about Christmas.

✤ Colour the pictures.

Coordinates:

1. I12 J13 I14 J14 K15 L14 M14 L13 M12 L12 K11 J12 I12

2. D7 A7 C9 B9 D11 C11 E13 G11 F11 H9 G9 I7 F7 F5 D5 D7

3. K8 L7 K6 L6 L3 J3 J6 K6 J7 K8

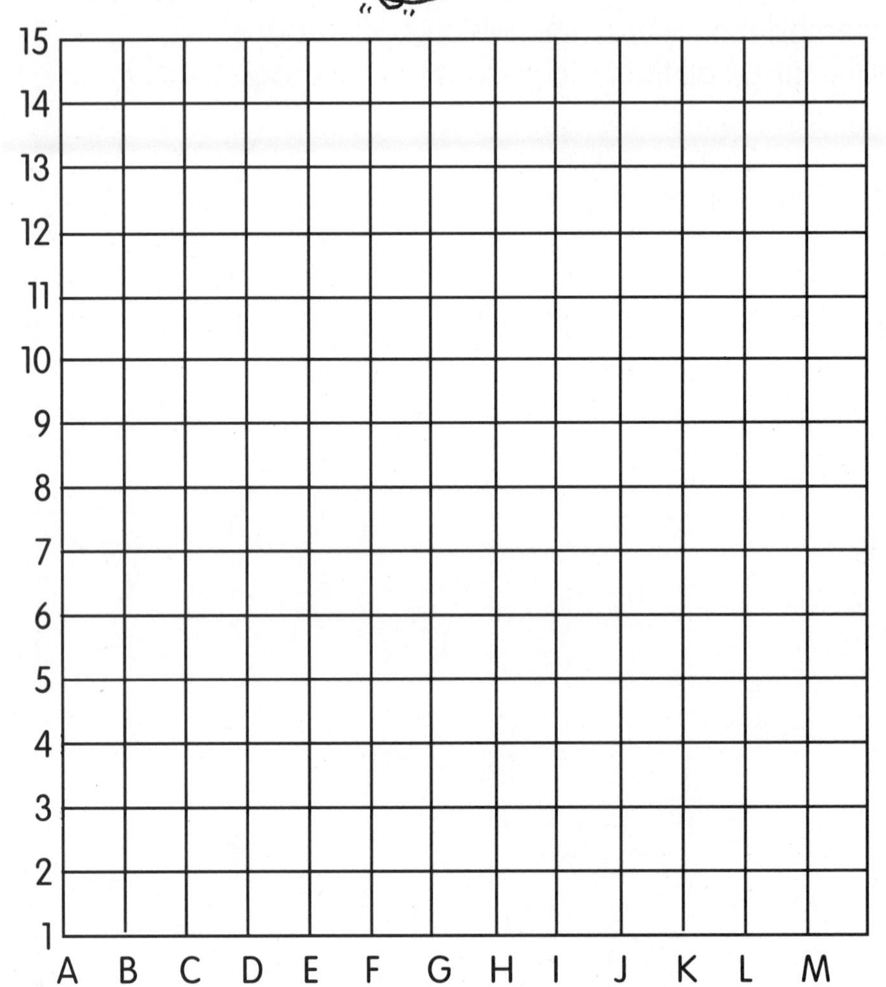

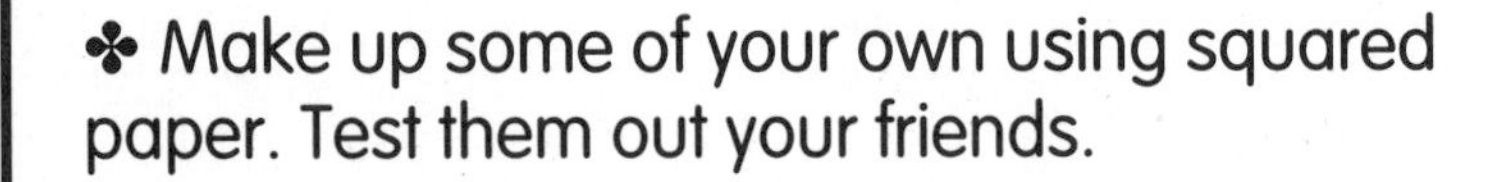

✤ Make up some of your own using squared paper. Test them out your friends.

Carol calculations

✤ Work out the answer to each problem. Find the answers below and write the corresponding letter above the number.

✤ When complete, the words will reveal the first line of a Christmas carol.

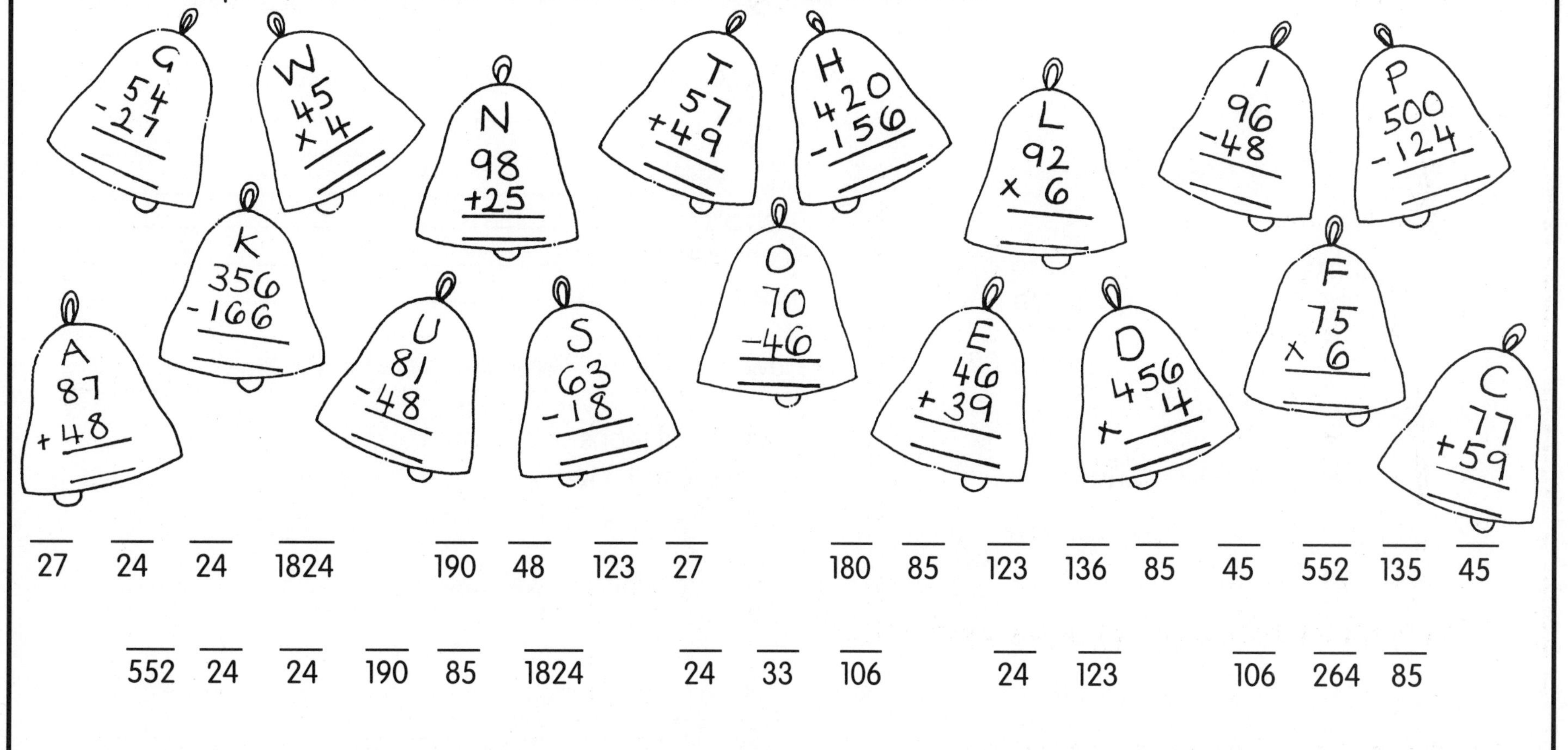

___ ___ ___ ___   ___ ___ ___ ___   ___ ___ ___ ___ ___ ___ ___ ___ ___
27 24 24 1824   190 48 123 27   180 85 123 136 85 45 552 135 45

___ ___ ___ ___ ___ ___   ___ ___ ___   ___ ___   ___ ___ ___
552 24 24 190 85 1824   24 33 106   24 123   106 264 85

___   ___ ___ ___ ___   ___ ___   ___ ___ ___ ___ ___ ___ ___
450   85 135 45 106   24 450   45 106 85 376 264 85 123

Name ____________

Christmas sale

Christmas Sale

Bargains Galore!!!

20% off these items:

t-shirts........................ were £15
jeans.......................... were £30
jackets........................ were £45
socks.......................... were £2

40% off these items:

dresses..................... were £30
skirts........................ were £25
tops.......................... were £10

DON'T DELAY BUY NOW !

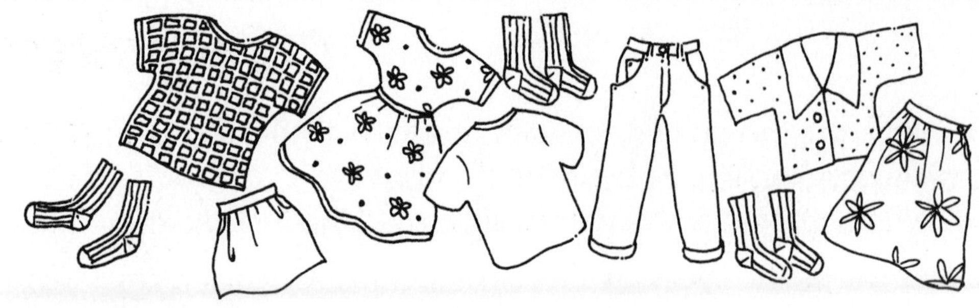

✤ What are the sale prices of these items?

– jeans ____________
– t-shirts ____________
– socks ____________
– dresses ____________
– skirts ____________

✤ How much would these items cost in the sale?

– 2 pairs of jeans and 1 t-shirt ____________
– 1 dress and 3 tops ____________
– 1 jacket and 2 skirts ____________

✤ How much change will there be from £50 for each of these items in the sale?

– 2 tops and 3 pairs of socks ____________
– 1 jacket ____________
– 2 skirts ____________

Dot-to-dot 2

✤ Work out each problem. Join up answer 1 to answer 2, answer 2 to answer 3, and so on until you have joined up all the answers.

✤ Finish the picture and colour it in.

1 32 + 24 = ___	**2** 53 + 25 = ___	**3** 51 + 24 = ___	**4** 44 +22 = ___	**5** 70 +29 = ___
6 34 + 13 = ___	**7** 20 + 19 = ___	**8** 80 + 12 = ___	**9** 43 + 25 = ___	**10** 21 +14 = ___
11 76 – 14 = ___	**12** 28 – 12 = ___	**13** 59 – 36 = ___	**14** 94 – 20 = ___	**15** 62 – 21 = ___
16 48 – 14 = ___	**17** 71 – 61 = ___	**18** 65 – 32 = ___	**19** 36 – 15 = ___	**20** 87 – 24 = ___
21 41 × 2 = ___	**22** 30 × 3 = ___	**23** 22 × 4 = ___	**24** 51 × 2 = ___	**25** 33 × 1 = ___
26 20 ÷ 5 = ___	**27** 18 ÷ 9 = ___	**28** 21 ÷ 3 = ___	**29** 12 ÷ 2 = ___	

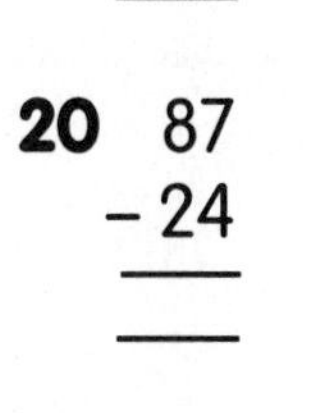

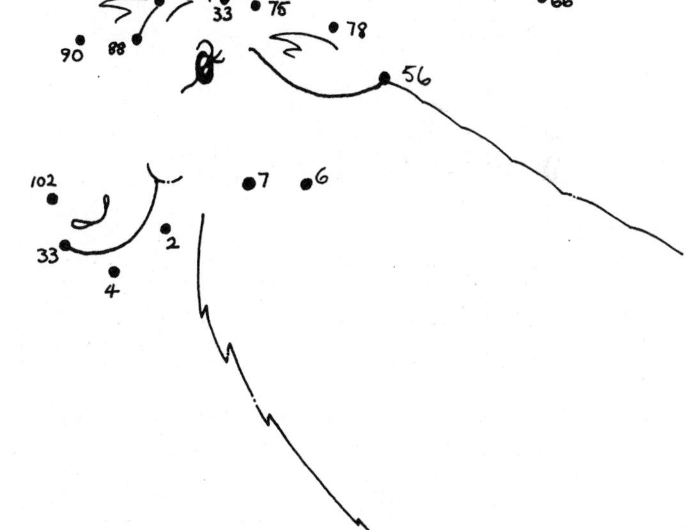

Name ____________

Christmas shopping

✤ Find the total cost of the items in each shopping bag.

clown	£8.99
fishing rod	£10.50
book	£3.99
ball	£2.50

baseball bat	£11.98
picture	£7.50
sunglasses	£5.99
toy plane	£4.50

record	£9.99
flowers	£12.50
perfume	£11.98
scarf	£6.50
teddy	£15.00

✤ Do your working out here:

Total cost: ____________

How much change will you have from £30? ____________

Total cost: ____________

How much change will you have from £30? ____________

Total cost: ____________

How much change will you have from £60? ____________

Name ____________________

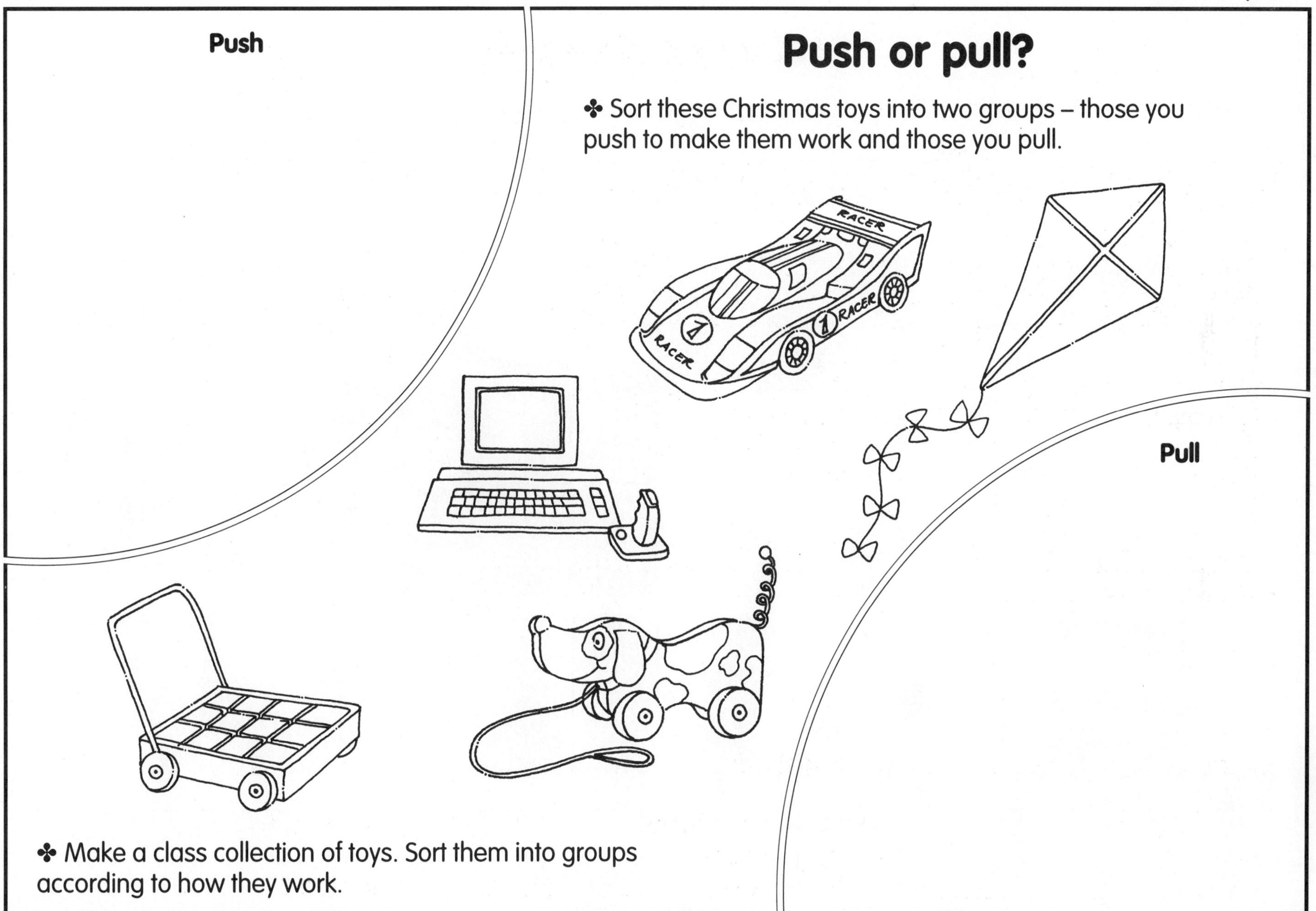

Push or pull?

✤ Sort these Christmas toys into two groups – those you push to make them work and those you pull.

✤ Make a class collection of toys. Sort them into groups according to how they work.

Name ____________________

Christmas I-spy

✤ Which of the following did you see last Christmas? Put a tick in the box.

✤ Write down any other things you would only see at Christmas time.

Name ____________________

Investigating materials

✤ What materials could these Christmas items be made from?

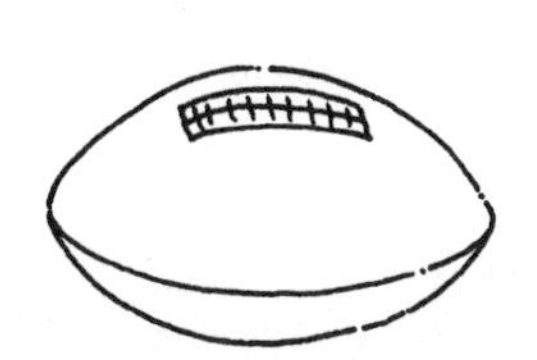

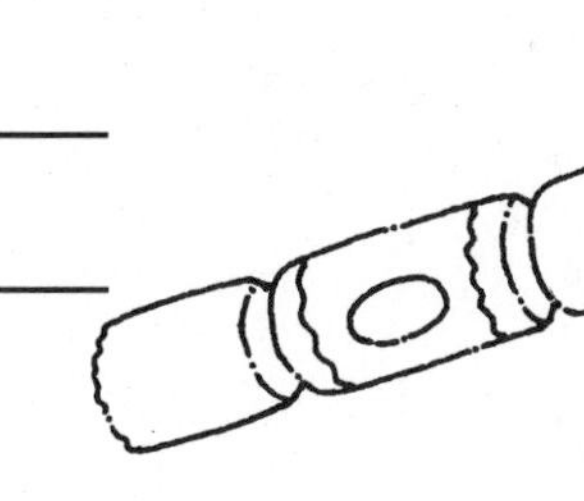

Name ______________

Footprints in the snow

Name ____________________

Safety at Christmas

✤ How many dangerous things can you spot in this picture?

✤ How would you make this room safer? ____________________

____

____

Name ________________

Movement

✤ Name the things in this Christmas scene that move. Describe how they move. The first one has been done for you.

Object	Movement
tree	sways

Name ____________________

Christmas music

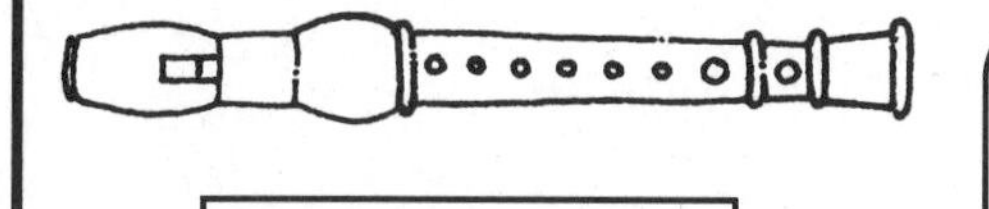

The school Christmas play used these instruments.

✤ What actions are needed to make them work?

✤ Choose from the list and write the name of the action in the space beside each instrument.

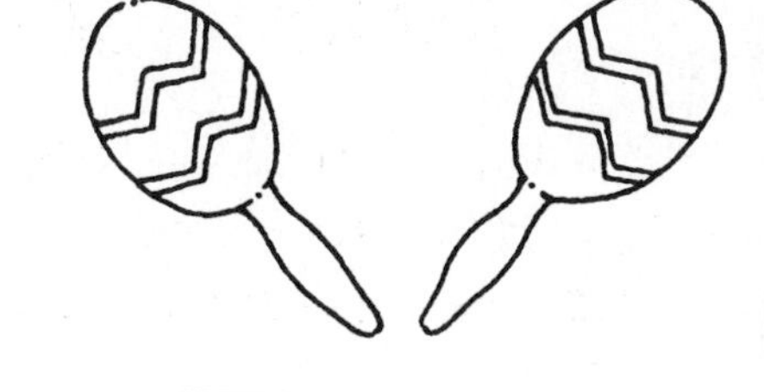

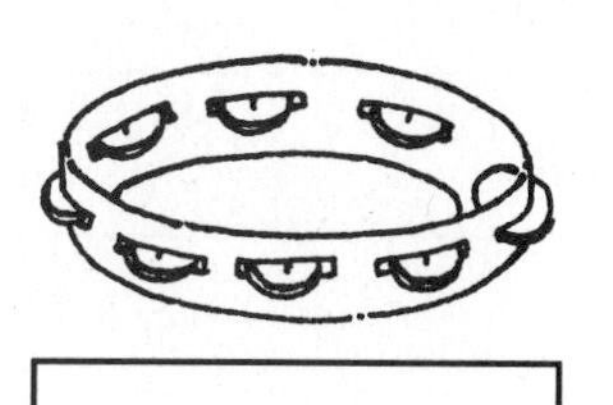

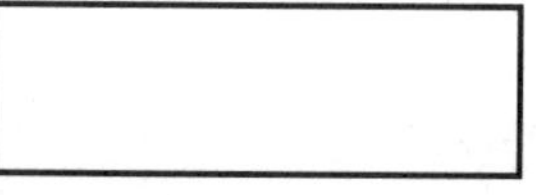

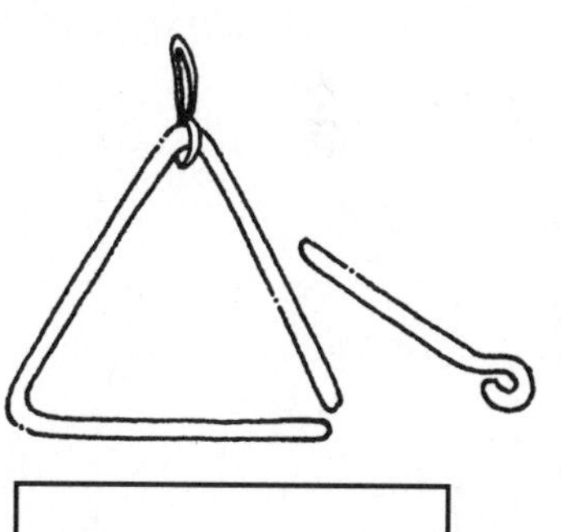

✤ Choose the actions from this list:

✤ Can you make instruments that would use all these actions?

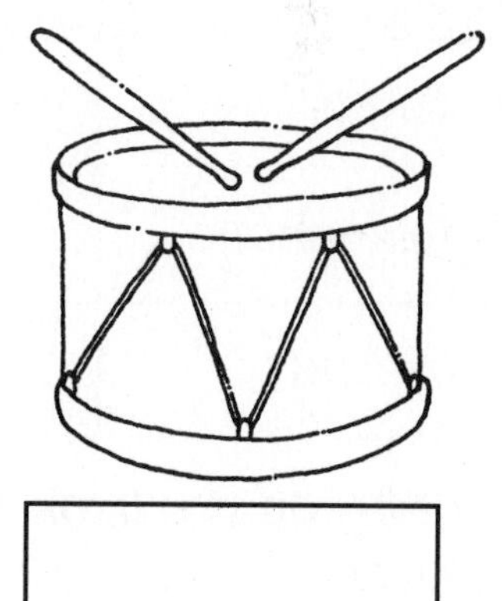

Name ______________

Paper chains

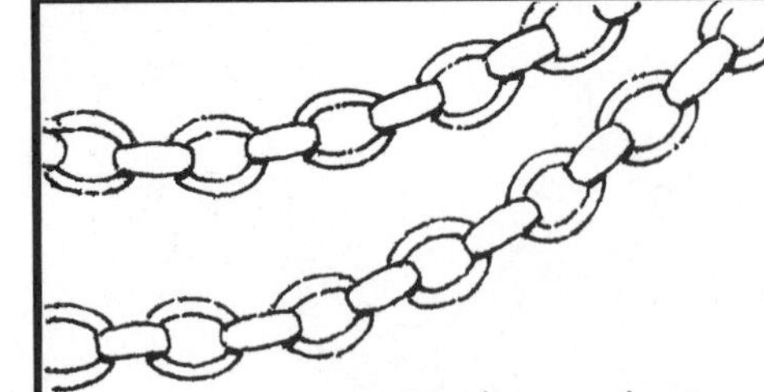

Paper chains

✤ Find the best type of paper to make paper chains.
What is the best way of fastening the paper chains together?

✤ Make a chain using these papers

Type of paper	Prediction Will it be suitable?	Result VG = Very Good; G = Good; P = Poor
Tissue		
Crepe		
Foil		
Cartridge		
Sugar		
Cellophane		
Writing		

✤ Why do you think your best paper was the most suitable?

____

✤ Use these fasteners to join the chains

Type of fastener	Prediction Will it be suitable?	Result VG = Very Good; G = Good; P = Poor
Sticky tape		
Paper clips		
Staples		
PVA glue		
Blu-Tack		
Pritt Stick		

✤ Which type of fastener is both strong and quick to use?

____

✤ Try out some other papers and fasteners. Decorate the room with your results!

Name ____________________

Candles

✤ Ask an adult to light a candle. Watch it closely as it burns. Draw your candle in the box on this page. Look closely at the shape of the flame. Describe what you can see happening to the candle as it burns.

____
____
____
____
____
____

✤ What do you think is happening when a candle burns? Why does it keep burning?

____
____
____
____

Name ____________________

Can you help Santa's elves?

Can you help Santa's elves?

Last Christmas, lots of children wanted magnets as presents. Santa was not very pleased with the way the elves had stored the magnets. When he went to pack them in his sack, all sorts of things were stuck to them! Poor Santa spent ages untangling them. This year, Santa has asked the elves to make sure that nothing magnetic is stored next to the magnets.

✤ Help the elves to sort out which of the following items should be stored away from the magnets.

✤ Predict which objects you think will be attracted to the magnet. Then test out the objects and write your results in the box provided. Then try out some different objects of your own.

Object	**Prediction** Will it be magnetic?	**Result** Is it magnetic?	Should it be stored next to the magnets?
Paper clip			
Mirror			
Scissors			
Brass weights			
Plastic ruler			
Aluminium foil			
Copper wire			
Rubber			
Nails			
Silver bracelet			

✤ What have you found out about magnetism?

____

____

____

✤ Does the magnet still work through paper, card, glass or wood?

____

____

____

Name ____________________

A waterproof sack for Santa

Santa needs a new sack, but it must be waterproof.
What is the best material to use?

How to find out:

✤ Collect an assortment of different fabrics – choose thick, thin, fluffy, smooth, textured, shiny and so on.

✤ Predict which ones you think will not let water soak through (waterproof materials). Then test them out to see if you are correct. Use an eye dropper to count the same number of drops of water you place on each fabric. Allow some time for the water to soak in.

✤ Look closely at each fabric with a hand lens. Can you think of a reason why some fabrics are waterproof and others are not? Which fabric do you think Santa should use?

Record your results here:

Type of fabric	**Prediction** Will it be waterproof?	**Result** Is it waterproof?

Conclusion:

____

____

Name ____________

What object is that?

What object is that?

✤ Use the identification key to work out which objects from the circle below belong in which box. Draw the objects in the boxes.

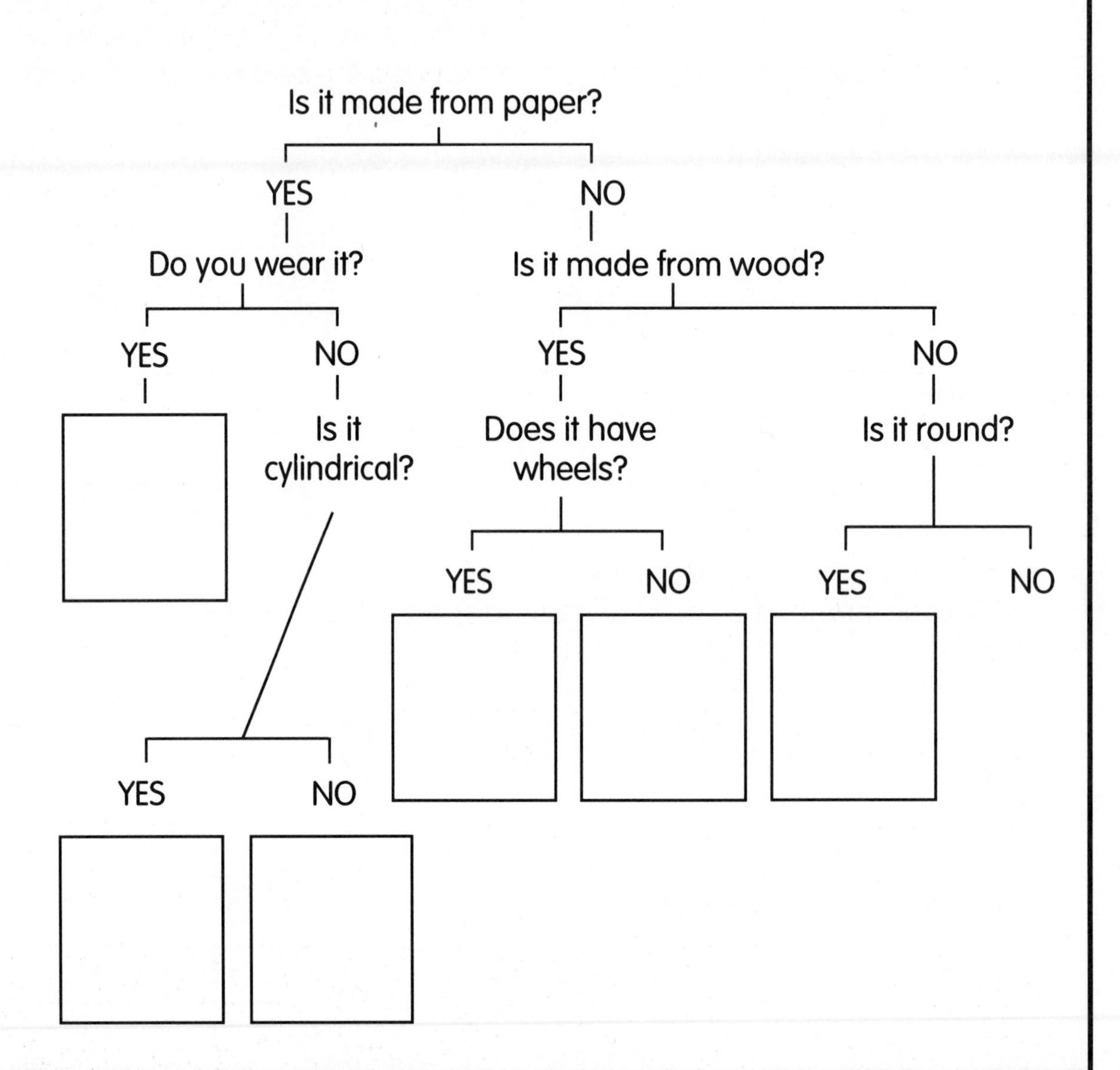

✤ Now make up your own key using a collection of Christmas toys or decorations.

Name ____________________

Holly observations

✤ Is your leaf rough or smooth? Shiny or dull? Describe it.

✤ Is your leaf all one colour?

✤ What are the edges like?

✤ Has anything been eating your leaf? Is it damaged in any way?

✤ Can you see any veins? Describe them.

✤ Is the back different to the front?

✤ What is the area of your leaf?

✤ How many points does your leaf have?

✤ Are there any marks on your leaf?

✤ Do other holly leaves have the same number of points?

✤ Describe the stem.

✤ Why do you think the leaf has these points?

✤ Measure your leaf. How long? How wide?

✤ Smell your leaf! Make a rubbing.

✤ Use a hand lens to make a detailed drawing.

Name ______________

Santa's elves each made a small Christmas tree. They wanted to have a light on top of the tree. They tried using a battery, bulb and wires. Try out each method they used to see which one works.

Method used	**Prediction** Will it light?	**Result** Did it light?
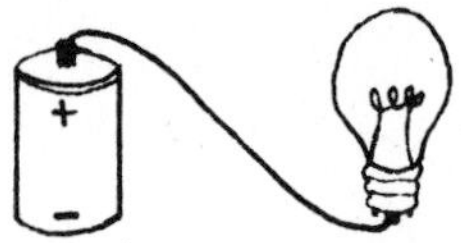		
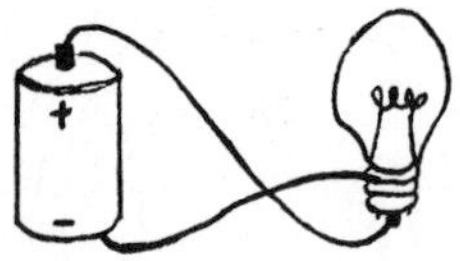		
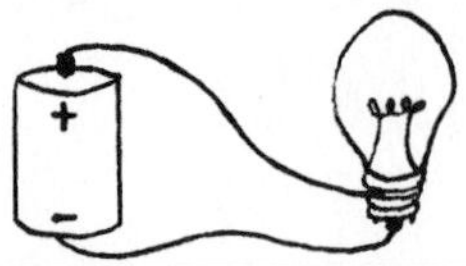		
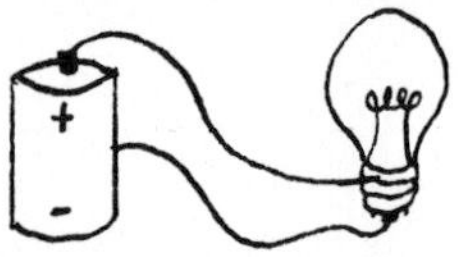		
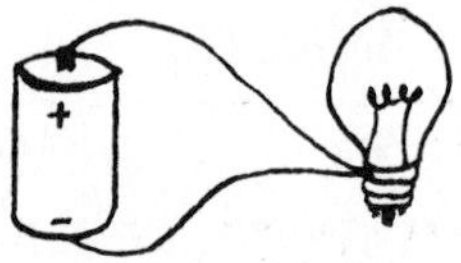		

After your experiment, answer these questions.

✤ Can you say how the light bulb works?

____

____

____

____

✤ What have you learned about making a circuit?

____

____

____

____

✤ On the back of this sheet, draw a circuit and use arrows to show the direction in which the electricity flows.

Santa's annual check-up

Every year before Christmas, Santa visits his doctor to have a check-up to see if he is fit enough to deliver all the presents.
Try out these activities to find out about your heart!

✤ Measure your heartbeat rate:
Find your pulse. Use two fingers (not thumb) and place them on your wrist or the front of your neck. Count the number of beats in 30 seconds then double this to find out how many beats per minute.
Measure your heart beat at rest then try out the exercises below to see how the rate changes.

Activity	**Me** Beats per minute	**My partner** Beats per minute
Rest		
20 arm swings		
10 sit-ups		
Step-ups for 1 minute		
Jogging for 2 minutes		

✤ Why do you think your heart beat changes with exercise?

____

____

____

____

____

____

✤ Compare your results with those of other children.

Christmas toys

Name ___________________

Christmas toys

✤ Match the shape with the toy.

Name ____________________

Following directions

✤ Colour the gifts correctly by following the directions.

Colour the one above **5** in blue.

Colour the one below **6** in yellow.

Colour the one to the right of **4** in red.

Colour the one to the left of **5** in yellow.

Colour the one to the left of **9** in blue.

Colour the one below **4** in green.

Colour the one above **6** in green.

Colour the one to the right of **5** in blue.

Colour the one above **4** in red.

Name ____________________

Mystery Christmas objects

All these objects have been drawn from above.

✤ Work out what they are. (They are all seen at Christmas time.)

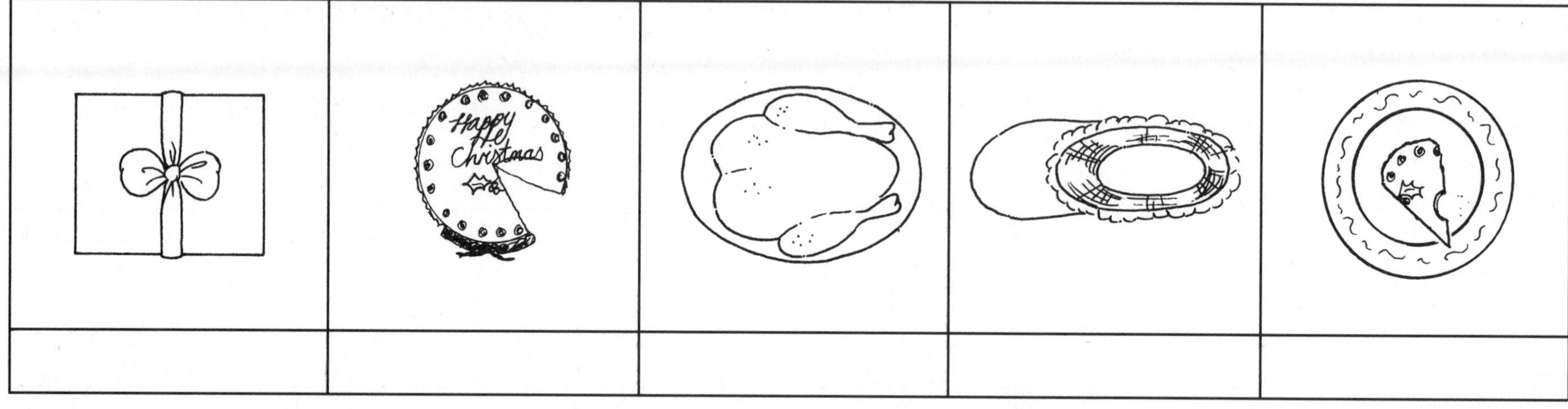

✤ Now draw some objects of your own, looking at them from above. Write the names of the objects underneath the drawing.

As Santa sees it!

When Santa flies over a town on his sleigh, he sees the world like this plan.

✤ Can you work out what each thing is?

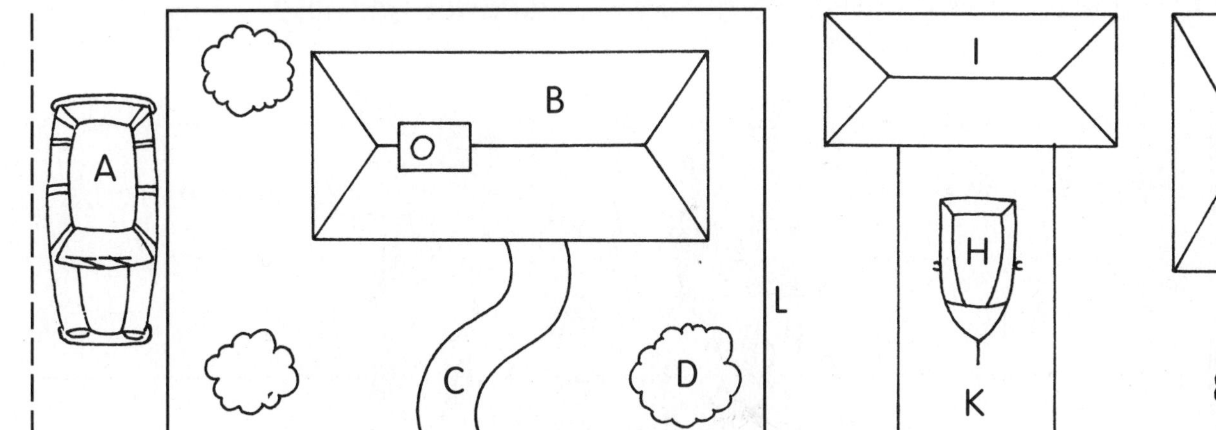

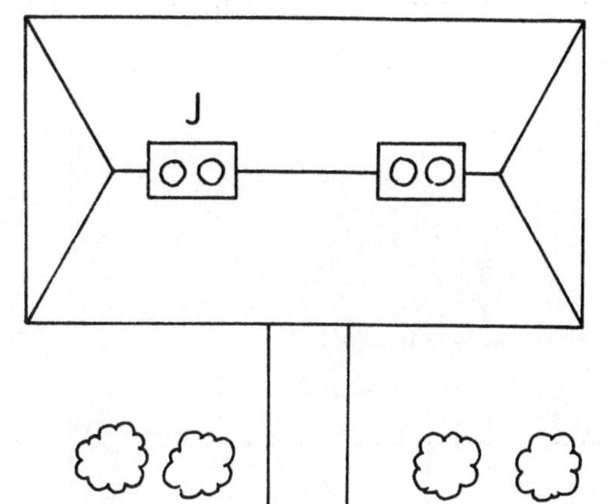

E

F

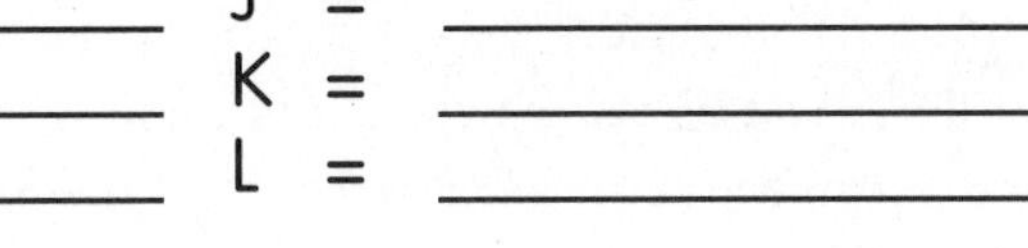

A = ____________________
B = ____________________
C = ____________________
D = ____________________
E = ____________________
F = ____________________

G = ____________________
H = ____________________
I = ____________________
J = ____________________
K = ____________________
L = ____________________

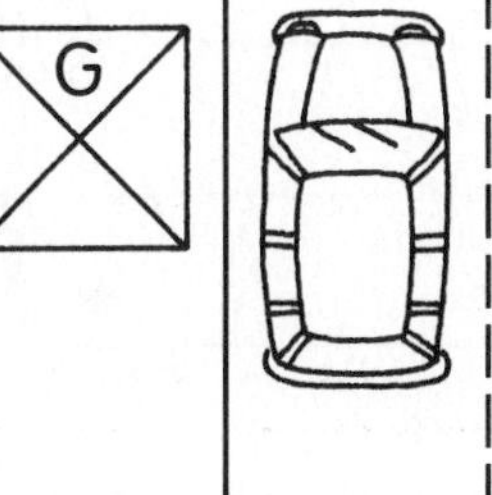

Choose from these:

house road tree boat

fence car telephone box

footpath garage driveway

chimney bicycle

Christmas around the world

Name ____________________

Christmas around the world

Christmas occurs during different seasons throughout the world. Each country celebrates Christmas in different ways with different traditions.

✤ Work out the countries shown in these drawings. Write the clues that helped you decide.

Country ____________________

Why I think this: ____________________

____

____

____

Country ____________________

Why I think this: ____________________

____

____

____

Country ____________________

Why I think this: ____________________

____

____

____

Country ____________________

Why I think this: ____________________

____

____

____

✤ Now draw a picture of Christmas in your country.

Santa's last stop

✤ Find out who Santa visited last of all when he went to Hollytown. Follow the directions:

- From Erin's house, he went LEFT and continued to the High Street.
- Then he went RIGHT until he reached Santa Road.
- He went RIGHT then RIGHT again.
- Then LEFT, LEFT, RIGHT and RIGHT again.
- He took the next RIGHT and then the second turn to the LEFT.

Who lives in this road?

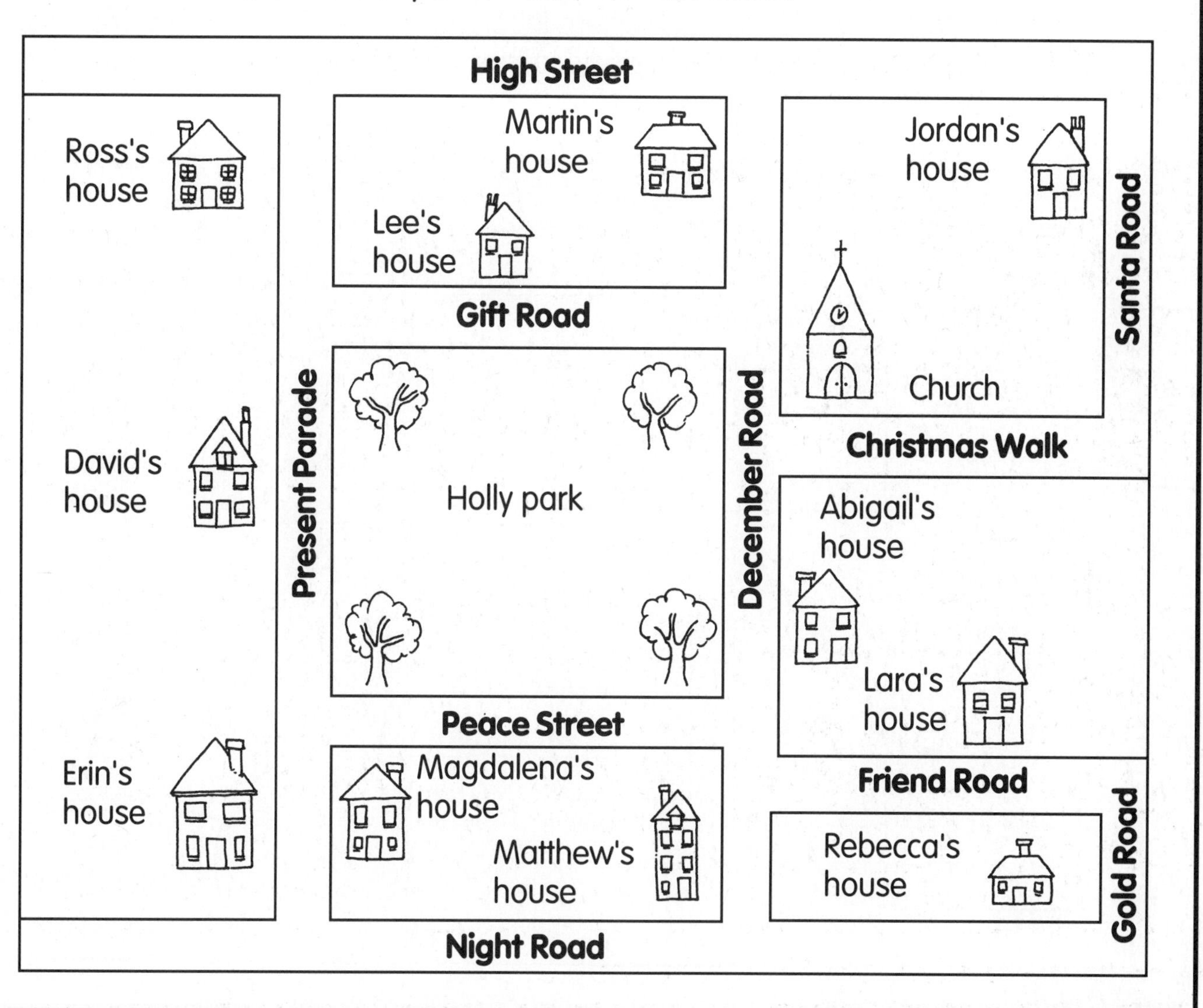

Name ____________

Help Santa's elves tidy up

Every Christmas Santa's workshop gets in a terrible mess.
The elves have to put everything back where it belongs.
✤ Can you help out by returning the objects to their correct places?
Here is the plan of Santa's workshop:

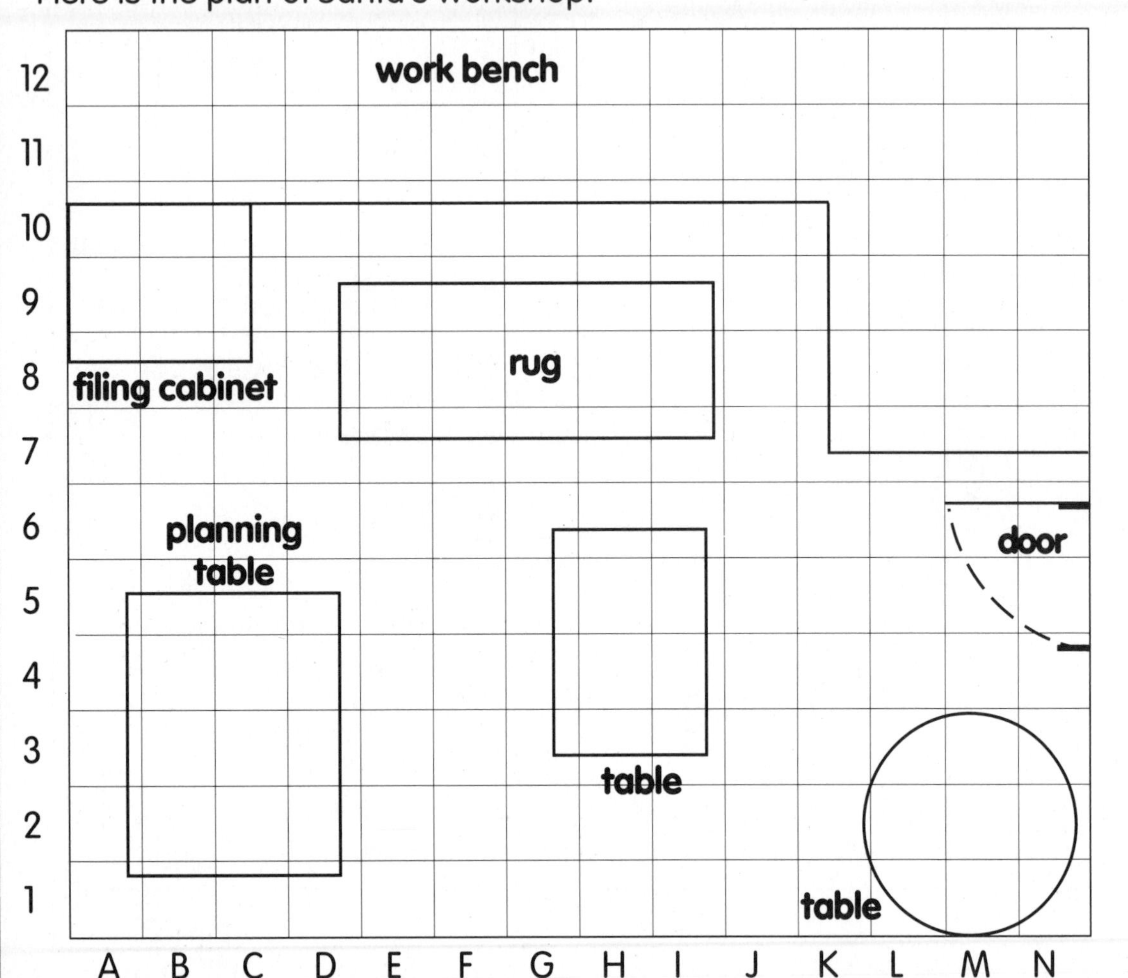

✤ Use the key to draw the objects in their correct place. The coordinates tell you where the items belong.

Coordinates

pot plants	M1, B9	plans	A9
pencil case	D2	glue	N10
hammers	I11, J11	rulers	D4, B4
cups	I4, I5, H4	paints	N8
saw	H12	paper	B2
nails	C12	ink	N7
scissors	L8	string	N12

Key

pot plant
scissors
hammer
glue
saw
paints
ruler

ink
paper
nails
pencil case
plans
cup
string

Name ____________

Christmas island

Santa loves to visit Christmas island. ✤ Work out how far he has to travel between each stop on the island.

How far is it (in kms) from

- ✤ House A to House B ________
- ✤ House B to House C ________
- ✤ House C to House D ________
- ✤ House D to House E ________
- ✤ House E to House F (via the Farm) ________
- ✤ House F to the Shops (via the Lake) ________

Scale: 1cm = 1km

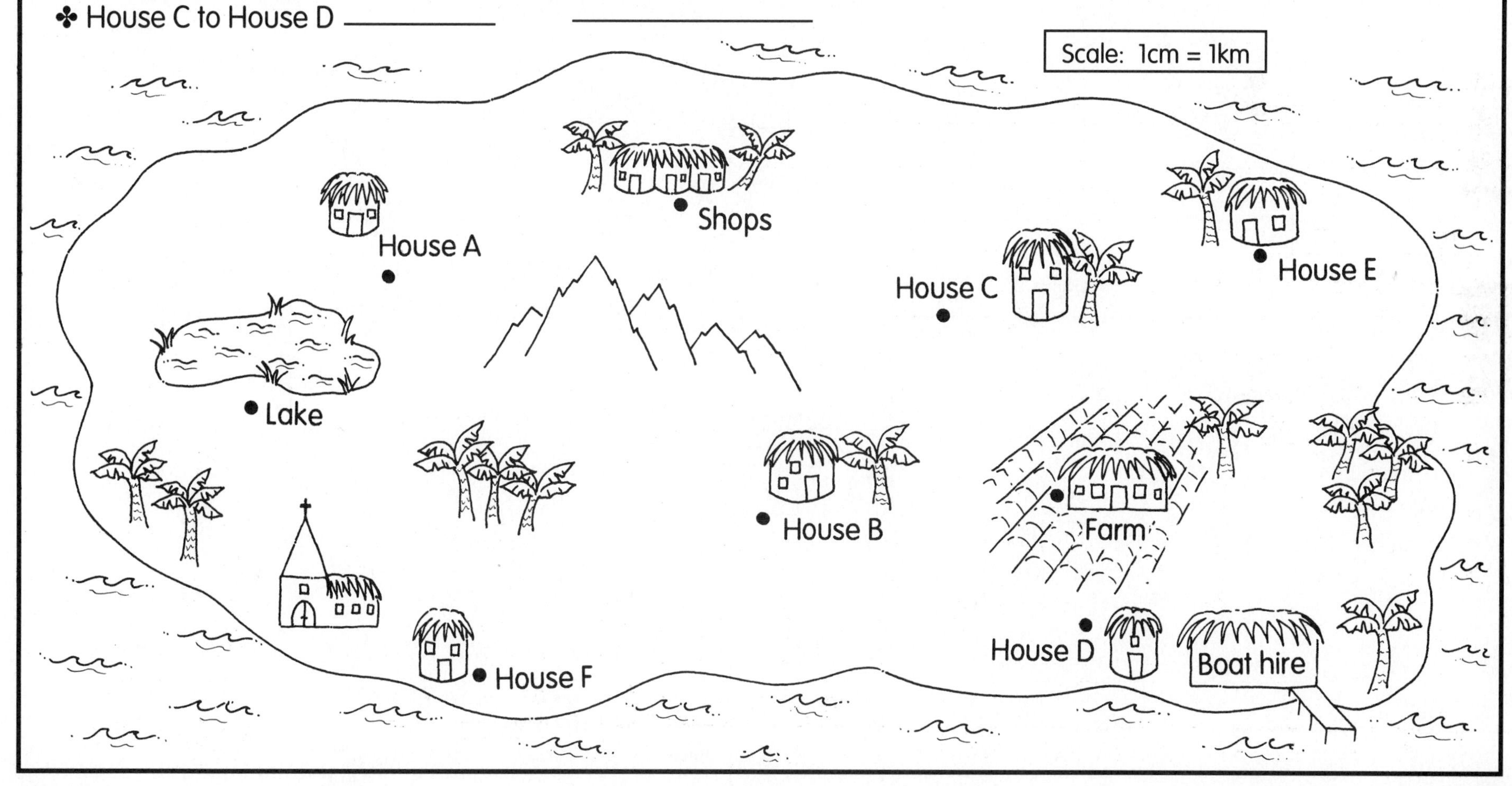

Name ______________

Christmas post

All these Christmas cards arrived at the Post Office without the country marked on them.

✤ Name the countries of these cities.

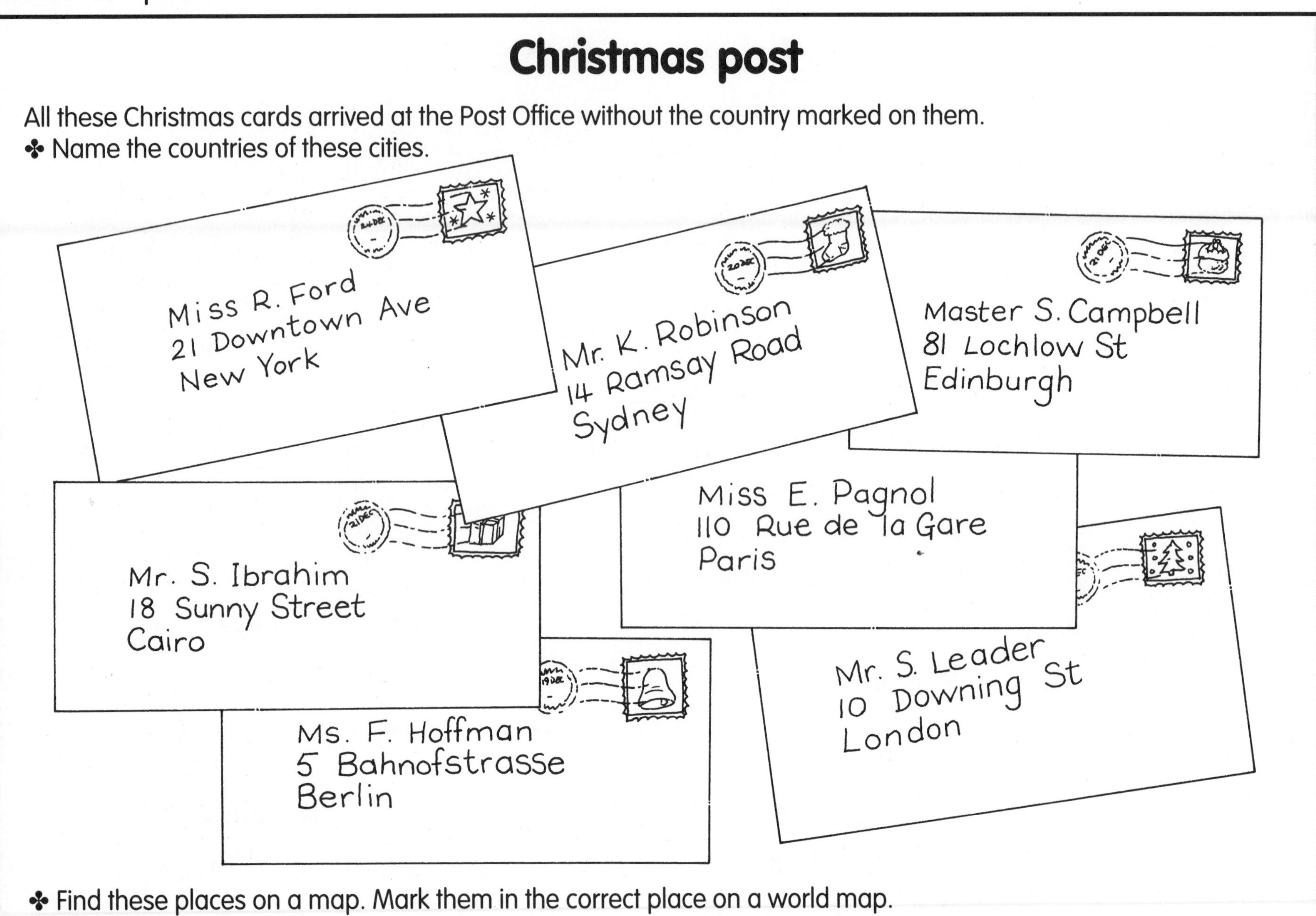

✤ Find these places on a map. Mark them in the correct place on a world map.

Name ____________________

Parcels for Christmas

✤ Draw a line connecting the parcel to the correct place on the map.

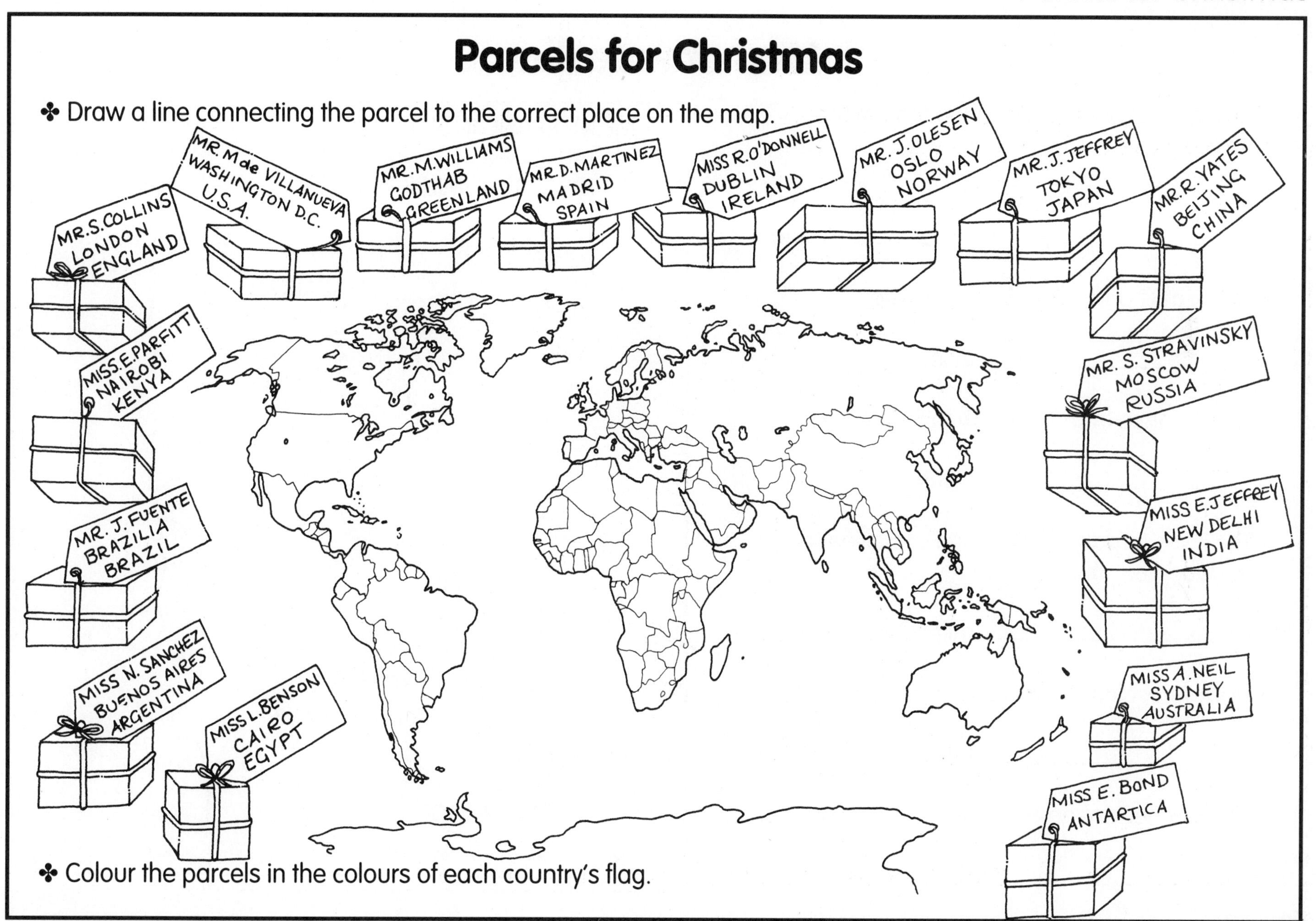

✤ Colour the parcels in the colours of each country's flag.

Name ____________________

Map of Palestine

This is a map of Palestine at the time of the birth of Jesus.

✤ Using the scale provided, work out the approximate distances in miles of the following:

- The widest part of the Sea of Galilee

  ____________________ miles.

- The distance from Nazareth to Bethlehem

  ____________________ miles.

- The River Jordan from the Sea of Galilee to the Dead Sea

  ____________________ miles.

- From Jerusalem to Bethlehem

  ____________________ miles.

- The Mediterranean coastline

  ____________________ miles.

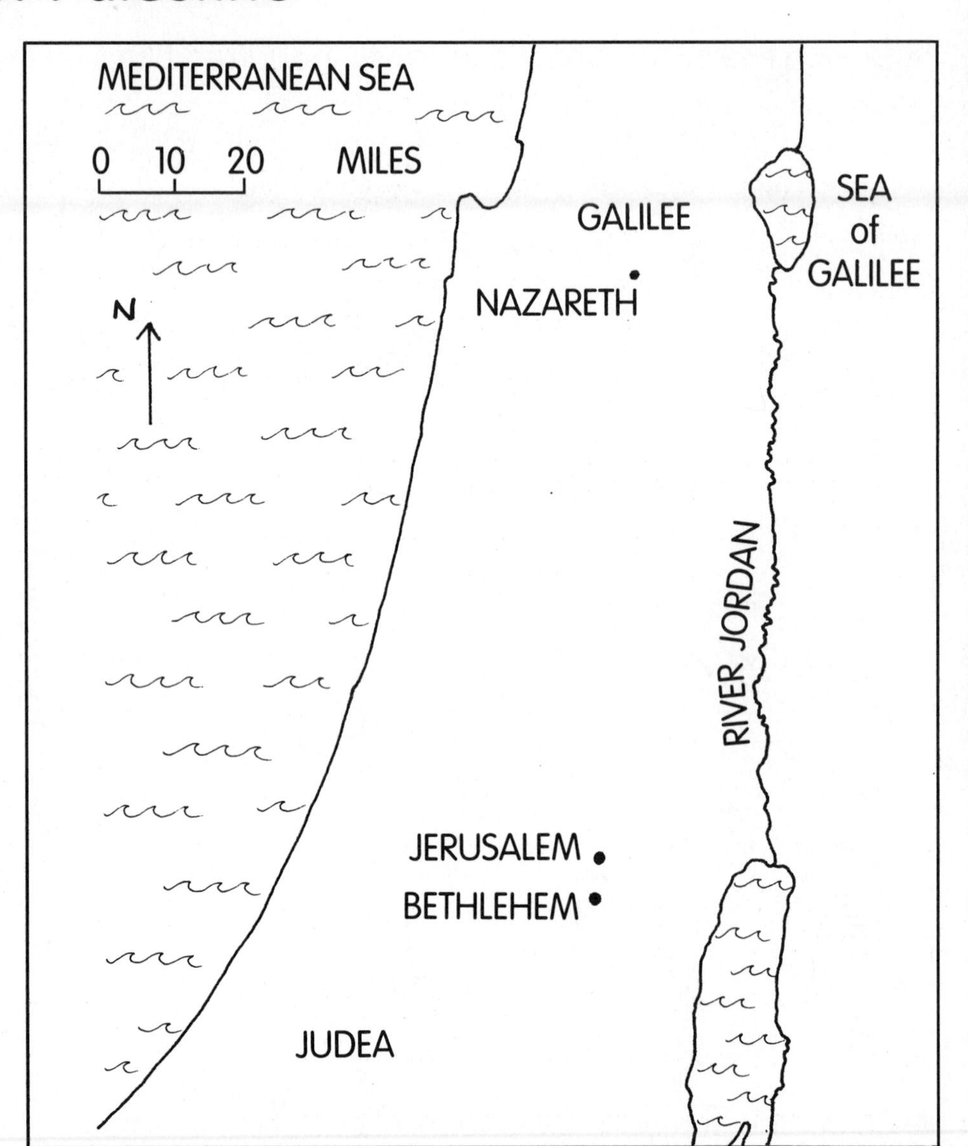

Santa's visit to Smithton

✤ Help Santa find his way around Smithton. He began his journey at David's house (A1).

- In which direction should he move in order to reach Jo's house? ________________
- Give the coordinates for Cameron's house. ________________________________
- From Gill's house, what direction should Santa move to visit the houses in Smith Street? ________________________
- Santa then visited the Burger bar. Give its coordinates. ________________________
- In which street is Bill's house? __________
- Who lives at F4? ________________
- Where does Julie live? ______________
- Who lives at F2? ________________
- From this house, in which direction must Santa move to get to Carol's house?

____

After delivering the presents, Santa thought he might have a rest in the park.

✤ Give directions to the park from Carol's house. ________________________

____

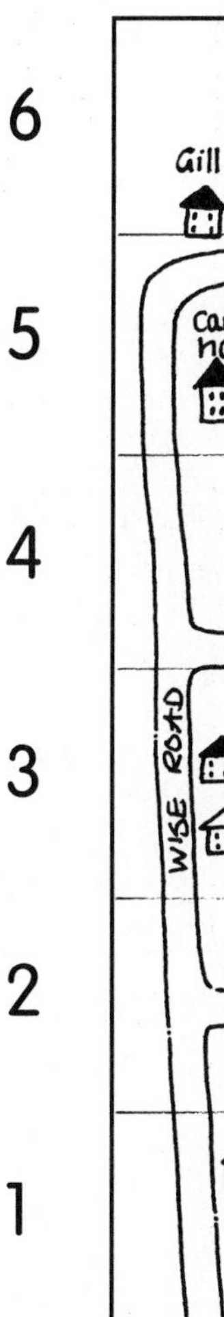

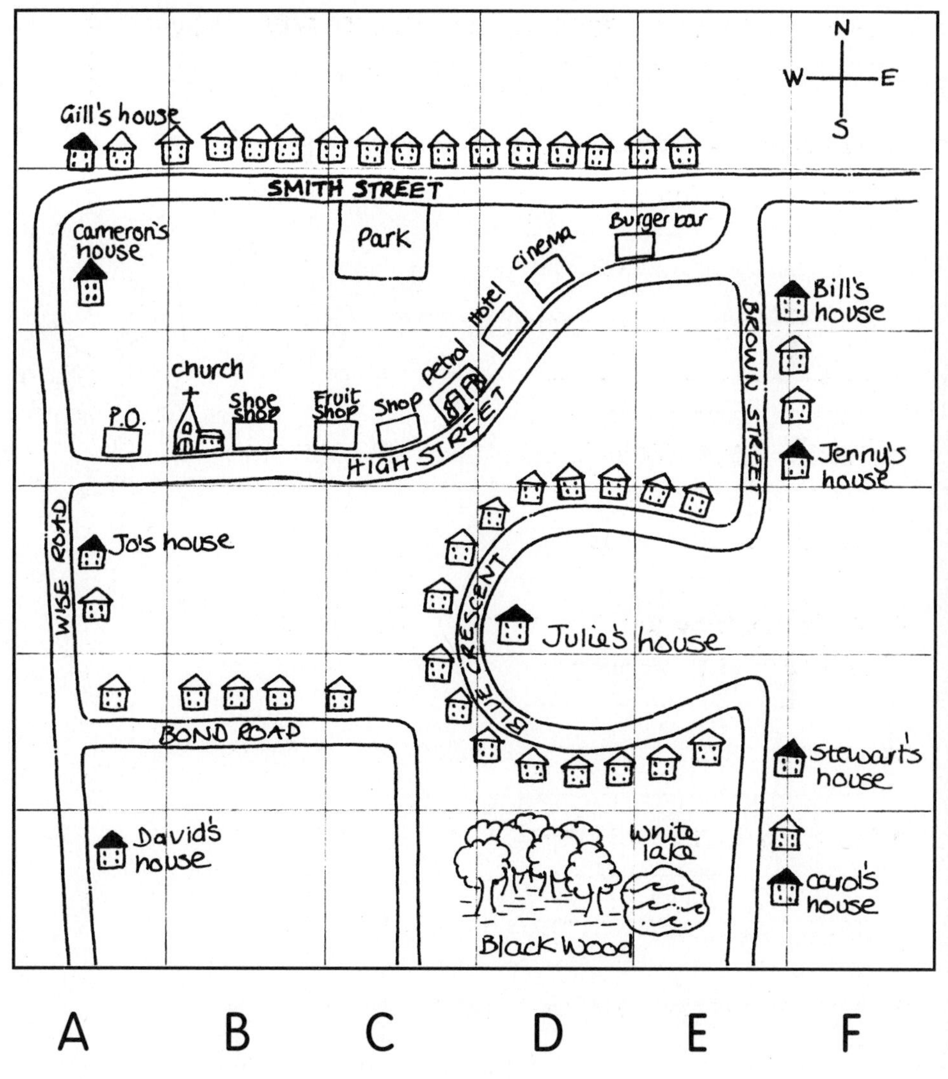

Name ____________________

Around the world with Santa

✤ Follow Santa's journey delivering presents all over the world. Use an atlas to find out the names of the countries he flies over.

✤ Write the names of the countries here:

1. ____________________
2. ____________________
3. ____________________
4. ____________________
5. ____________________
6. ____________________
7. ____________________
8. ____________________
9. ____________________
10. ____________________
11. ____________________
12. ____________________
13. ____________________
14. ____________________
15. ____________________
16. ____________________
17. ____________________
18. ____________________
19. ____________________
20. ____________________

To the North Pole

A 1 2 3 B 4 5 C 6 7 8 D 9 10 11 12 13 14 E 15 F 16 G 17 18 19 20

N

✤ Name the oceans and seas Santa passes over.

A ____________________
B ____________________
C ____________________
D ____________________
E ____________________
F ____________________
G ____________________

The weather on Christmas Day

This is a weather forecast for Europe on Christmas Day.

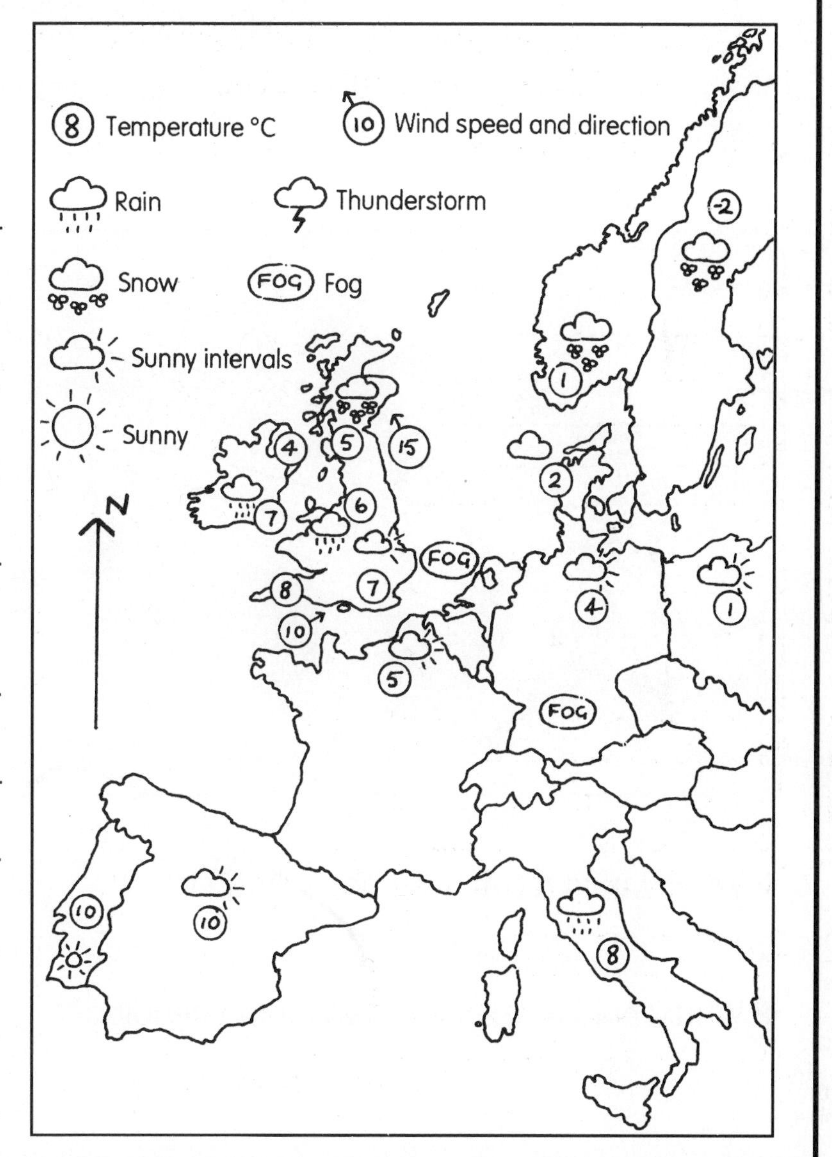

✤ Answer the following questions. Use an atlas to help you.

✤ What temperature will it be in London? ________________

✤ In which country will it be –2°C? ________________

✤ In which country will it be sunny? ________________

✤ In which countries will it snow? ________________

✤ What temperature will it be in Rome? ________________

✤ In what direction will the wind be blowing from in Scotland? ________________

✤ Where will it be foggy? ________________

✤ What will the temperature be in Paris? ________________

✤ In which countries will it rain? ________________

✤ Which place will have the highest temperature? ________________

✤ In which countries will it be only 1°C? ________________

Name ____________

Baby beds

This is a picture of the type of bed baby Jesus slept in. It is called a crib.

✤ Use this space to draw a bed that a baby might sleep in today.

✤ What would a crib have been made from?

✤ What could have been used for the bedding?

✤ What would the modern bed be made from?

✤ Are there any things that are the same?

Name ____________________

The birth of Jesus

✤ Colour the pictures and cut them out. Put them in the right order to tell the story.

Name ______________

Old or new?

Name ____________________

Biblical clothing

This is the type of clothing men wore in Palestine when Jesus was born.

✤ What are the differences and similarities between the Biblical clothing and clothes worn today in our country?

____

____

____

____

✤ Why do you think men wore long flowing garments?

____

____

____

____

✤ Draw a picture of the clothes men wear today in our country.

✤ Find out if any countries still wear similar clothing to this today.

Name ____________________

A Christmas time-line

A Christmas time-line

This page contains nine facts about Christmas customs.

✤ Cut them out and put them in the correct order to make a time-line.

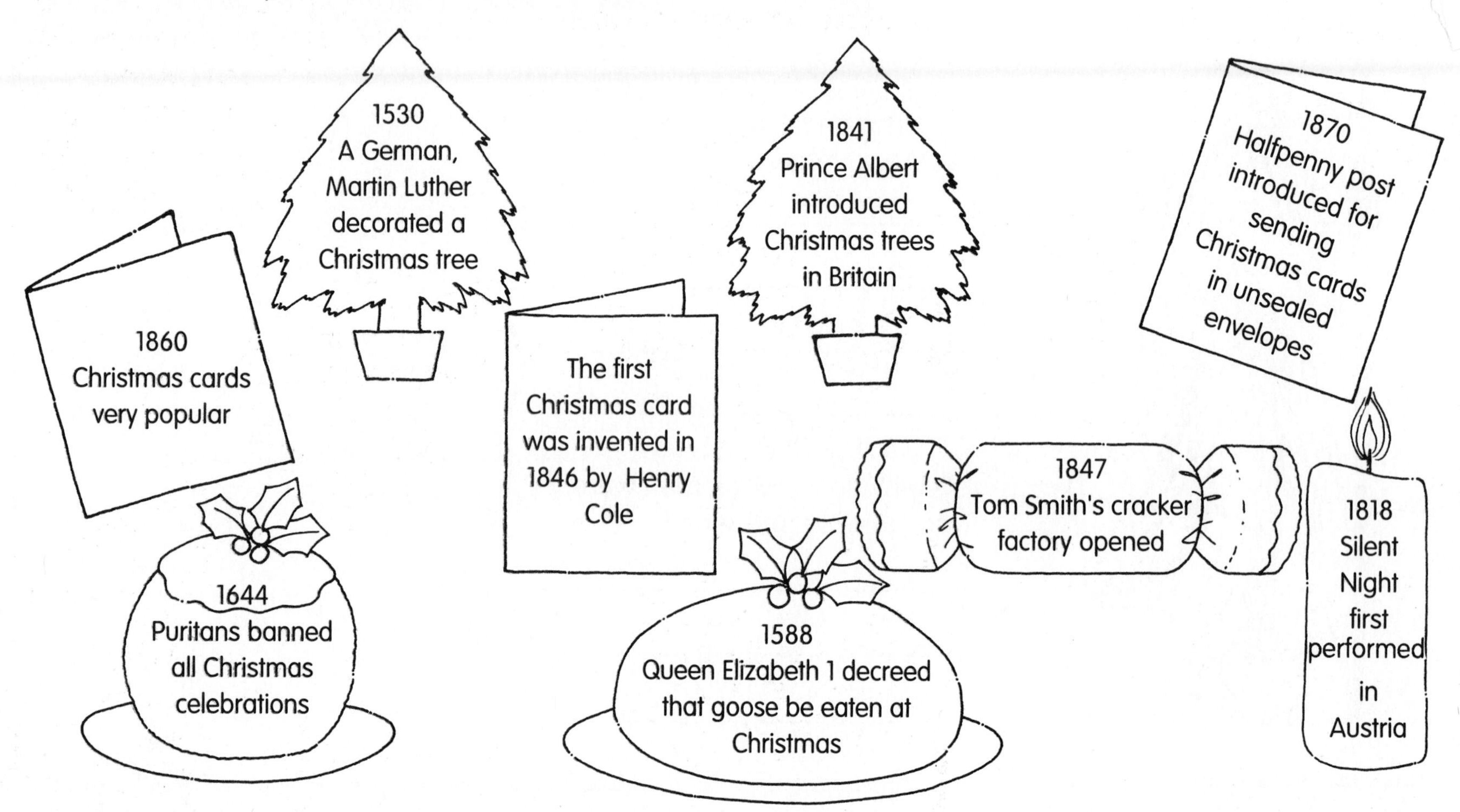

✤ Find out about other Christmas customs and when they were introduced.

Name ____________________

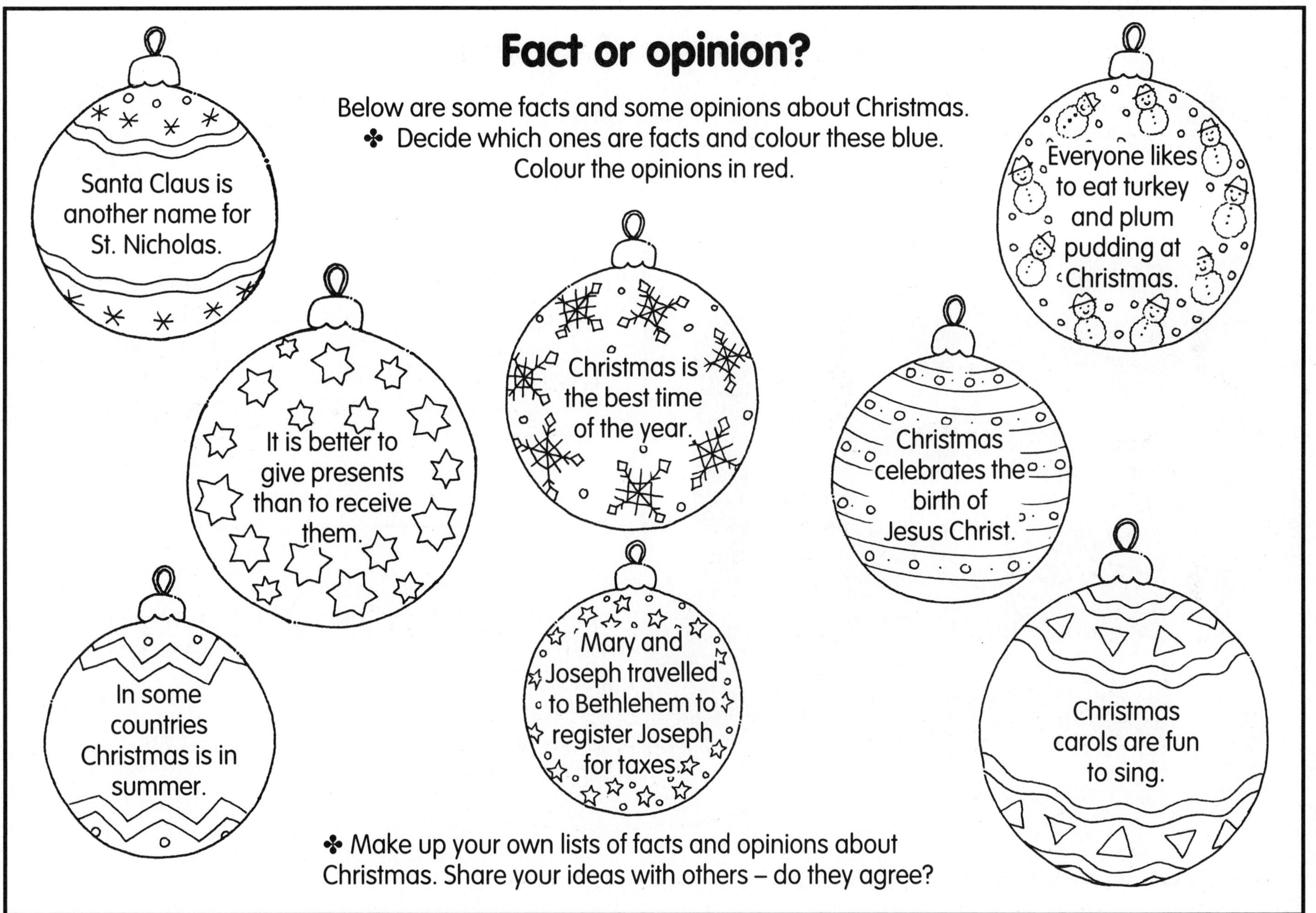

Fact or opinion?

Below are some facts and some opinions about Christmas.

✤ Decide which ones are facts and colour these blue. Colour the opinions in red.

✤ Make up your own lists of facts and opinions about Christmas. Share your ideas with others – do they agree?

Name ____________________

The history of Christmas

The history of Christmas

• a crossword •

1				■	2	■	3	■	4	■	■
■	■	■	■	5				R			6
■	■	■	■	■		■		■		■	
■	7	■	8					■		■	
■	U	■	■	■		■	■	■		■	
9				K				■		■	
■		■	■	■		■	■	■	H	■	
■		■	■	■	■	■	■	■		■	■
10 W							■	■		■	■
■		■	■	■	■	■	■	■	■	■	■
■	11						N				

Across:

1. A log of wood traditionally burned on Christmas Eve.
5. The name of the town where Mary lived.
8. The king of Judaea at the time of Jesus' birth.
9. Tom Smith's factory first made these in 1847.
10. A bowl filled with ale and passed around the lord's manor in Saxon times.
11. A carol first performed in Austria in 1818 (6, 5).

Down:

2. The angel who visited Mary.
3. Invented by Henry Cole in 1846, the Christmas _____
4. The town where Mary and Joseph went to register for taxes.
6. Wrote the music, The Messiah.
7. The people who banned Christmas in the 1640s in England.

Name ________________

Christmas in my grandparents' day

✤ Ask your grandmother, grandfather or an elderly friend these questions to find out what Christmas used to be like.

Interview questions:

Q What kinds of presents did you receive as a child?
A ________________

Q How much money did you have for buying gifts?
A ________________

Q What kinds of decorations did you put up?
A ________________

Q Did your school have Christmas concerts?
A ________________

Q How many days holiday did you have at Christmas?
A ________________

Q What food did you eat on Christmas Day?
A ________________

Q Did you help with the preparations?
A ________________

Q Did you go to church?
A ________________

Q What was your favourite carol?
A ________________

Q What did you do on Christmas Eve?
A ________________

Q What was your Christmas tree like?
A ________________

Q What did you enjoy most at Christmas?
A ________________

✤ Compare these answers to what Christmas is like today.

Name ______________

Christmas cards

The picture below shows the kind of scenes featured on early Christmas cards.

The very first Christmas card was printed in 1846 and was the idea of Henry Cole, the director of the Victoria and Albert Museum in London.

✣ Look carefully at the picture then answer the questions on the right-hand side of this page.

✣ What is the family in the centre of the card doing?

____

____

✣ What is happening in the other two drawings?

____

____

✣ In what way is the card similar to today's cards?

____

____

✣ How is the card different to today's cards?

____

____

✣ What things do today's cards have on the front?

____

____

Name ____________________

Christmas party dressing

These pictures show what might have been worn to Christmas celebrations in different historical periods.

✤ Work out which period each one represents. Use reference books to help you.
✤ Colour, cut out and place each one in chronological order.

Name ________________

Christmas in the past

This is a drawing of a Victorian household at Christmas.

✤ What do you think they are doing?

___

___

✤ What clues are there to tell you what room they are in?

___

___

✤ How does the clothing differ from what we wear today?

___

___

✤ What things can you see that are similar today?

___

___

✤ How would the task they are doing be done today?

___

___

Christmas research

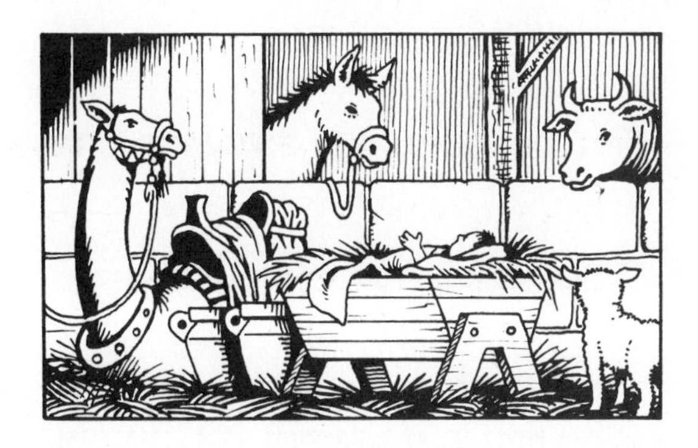

✤ Find out the answers to the following questions:

✤ Where did Mary and Joseph live before Jesus was born?

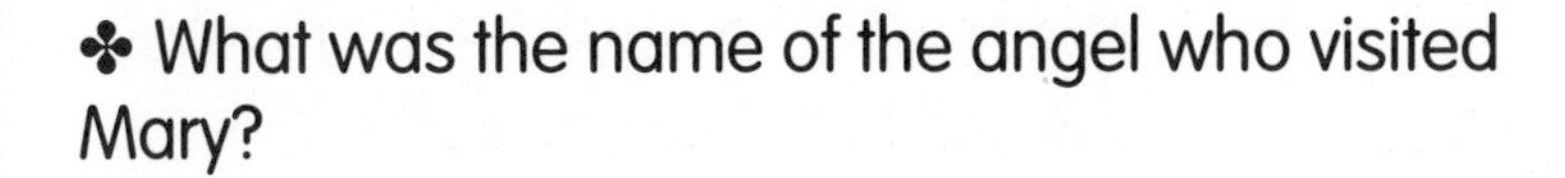

✤ What was the name of the angel who visited Mary?

✤ Why did Mary and Joseph travel to Bethlehem?

✤ Why was Jesus born in a stable?

✤ What was Jesus wrapped in after He was born?

✤ Why did the shepherds visit Jesus?

✤ Who was the King of Judaea when Jesus was born?

✤ How did the three Wise Men find Jesus?

✤ What gifts did the Wise Men give to Jesus?

✤ Where did King Herod live?

✤ Who was the Emperor of Rome when Jesus was born?

✤ What is the name of the river that flows from the Sea of Galilee to the Dead Sea?

✤ What did the Wise Men do after they had seen Jesus?

Name ____________

Christmas customs

✤ Find out about the following Christmas traditions:

✤ When does Advent begin?

____

✤ Who first introduced Christmas trees to Britain?

____

✤ When was the first Christmas card printed?

____

✤ Who invented Christmas crackers?

____

✤ What other names is Santa Claus known by?

____

✤ What was a wassail bowl?

____

✤ When is Epiphany? Who is remembered on that day?

____

✤ What is the day after Christmas called? Why is it called this?

____

____

✤ Who was Boniface? What is he best known for?

____

✤ What is a Yule log?

____

✤ What are mummers?

____

Name ___________________

The Christmas Story

Luke, Chapter 2, Verses 1, 3-12

✤ Fill in the missing words. Use a bible to help you.

At that time the __________ Augustus ordered a ______________ to be taken throughout the Roman _________ . Everyone, then, went to _____________ himself, each to his own town.

Joseph went from the town of____________ in ____________ to the town of Bethlehem in Judaea, the birthplace of King _____________. Joseph went there because he was a _____________ of David. He went to register with __________ who was promised in marriage to him. She was pregnant, and while they were in ____________ , the time came for her to have her ___________ . She gave birth to her first _____________ , wrapped him in strips of _____________ and laid him in a __________ – there was no room for them to stay in the_____ .There were some ______________ in that part of the country who were spending the_________ in the fields, taking care of their _________ . An __________ of the Lord appeared to them, and the glory of the Lord __________ over them. They were terribly ________, but the angel said to them, 'Don't be afraid! I am here with good __________ for you, which will bring great _____to all the people. This very day in David's town your Saviour was ________ – ________ the Lord! And this is what will prove it to you: you will find a __________ wrapped in strips of cloth and lying in a __________ .'

✤ Illustrate the story.

Name ____________________

Gift tags

Gift tags

✤ Add pictures, patterns, shapes and colours.
Design some other gift tags of your own.

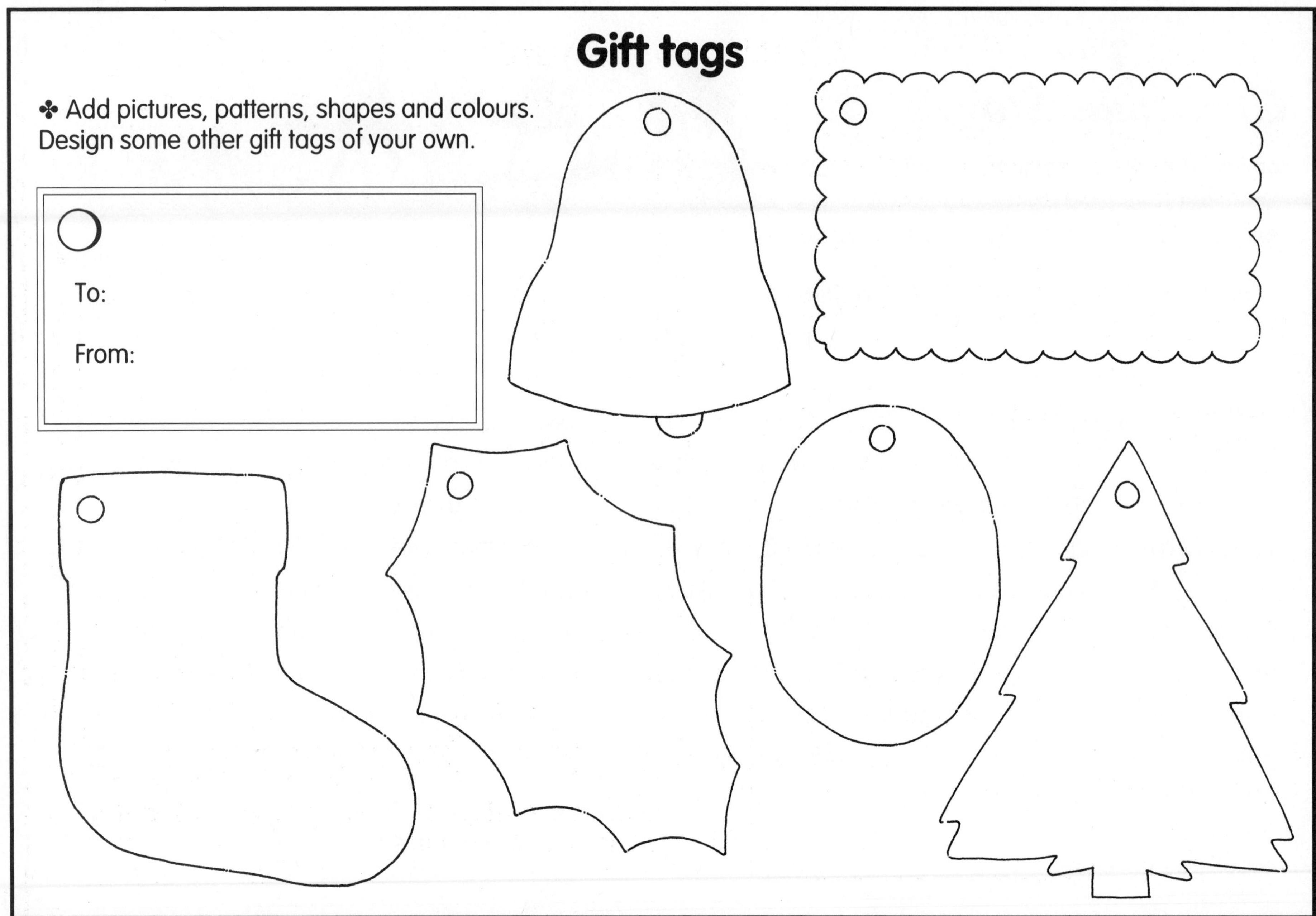

Christmas stamps

Look at the design of some Christmas stamps. There have been many different types. Some have used animals, people and places and some have used Christmas scenes.

✤ Think about the sort of design you would like to see on a stamp this Christmas. Use the space on the right to try out some designs.

✤ Now evaluate your designs. How might they be improved?

✤ Use the envelope on the left to design a Christmas scene for a first day cover.

Name ________________

Christmas advertising

✤ Design an advertisement to sell a fantastic new toy on sale at Christmas. Before you begin, use these questions to help you plan it:

✤ What drawings will I have?

____

____

✤ What will the slogan or catch-phrase be?

____

____

✤ What special features of the toy do I want to mention?

____

____

✤ What will the largest words say?

____

Name ________________

New Christmas toy!

✤ What new toys would you like to be invented?

____

____

✤ Do a survey in your class to find out what toys other people would like.

✤ Choose one of these ideas and design this toy.

✤ Draw your design in this space.

✤ Show a front, back and side view.

✤ What is the name of your toy?

____

✤ Invent a company name. What is it?

____

✤ What special features does your toy have?

____

✤ Now make your toy!

My design

Name ______________

Plan a Christmas party

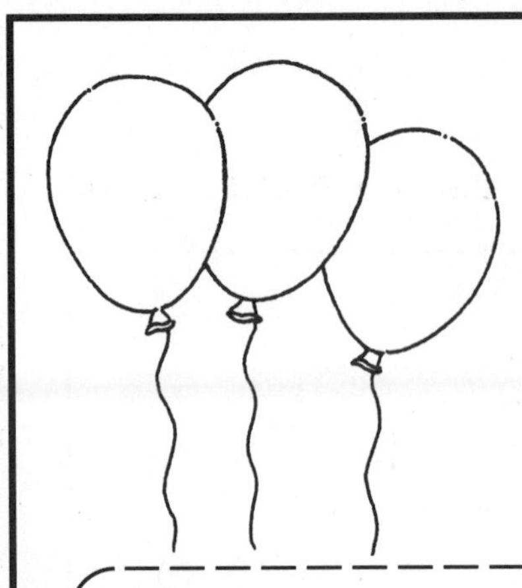

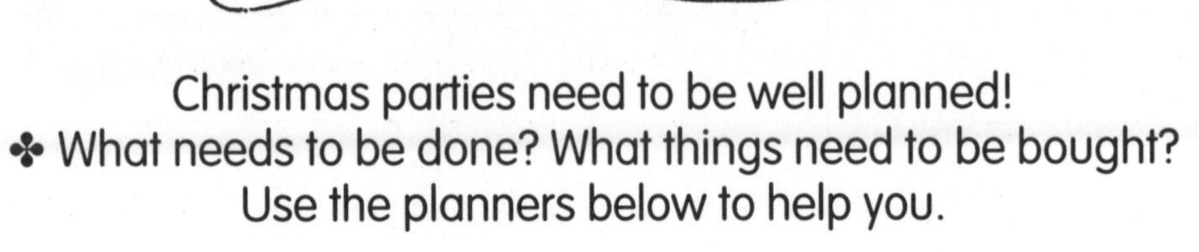

Christmas parties need to be well planned!
✤ What needs to be done? What things need to be bought?
Use the planners below to help you.

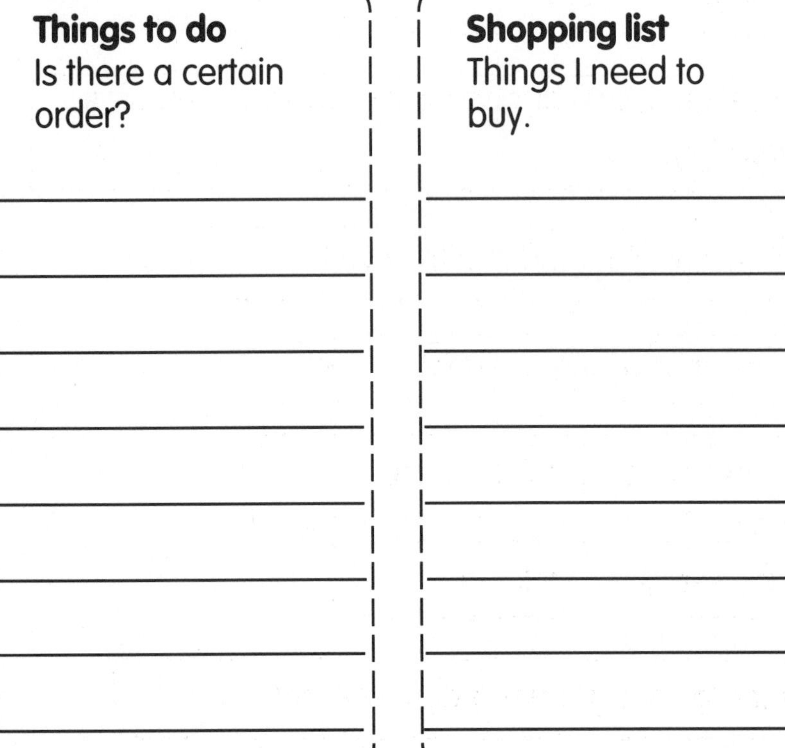

Things to do
Is there a certain order?

Shopping list
Things I need to buy.

Menu
What food will I prepare?

Games
What will we do?

Name ___________________

Christmas cake recipe

✤ Cut out the sentences below and rearrange them in the correct order for making the cake. Compare your version with those of your friends – do they agree?

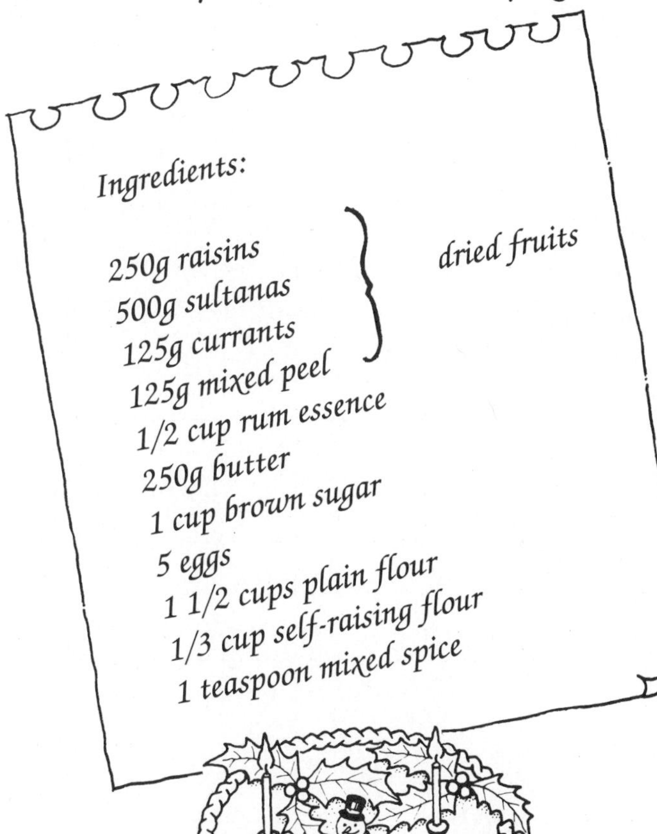

Pour mixture into cake tin.

Add flour to the egg/dried fruit mixture.

Sift the flours and spice.

Mix rum essence and dried fruit in a bowl. Cover. Let it stand overnight.

Add egg mixture to dried fruit. Mix well.

Line a cake tin with greaseproof paper.

Bake in slow oven for 3-3 1/2 hours.

Collect and weigh dried fruits.

Beat butter, add sugar and eggs, one at a time.

✤ Now bake it!

Name ____________________

Designing Christmas decorations

- ✤ Use this page to design your own decorations by colouring different parts of the pattern.
- ✤ Do your shapes tessellate? Are they symmetrical?
- ✤ Make your Christmas design with coloured paper and glitter.

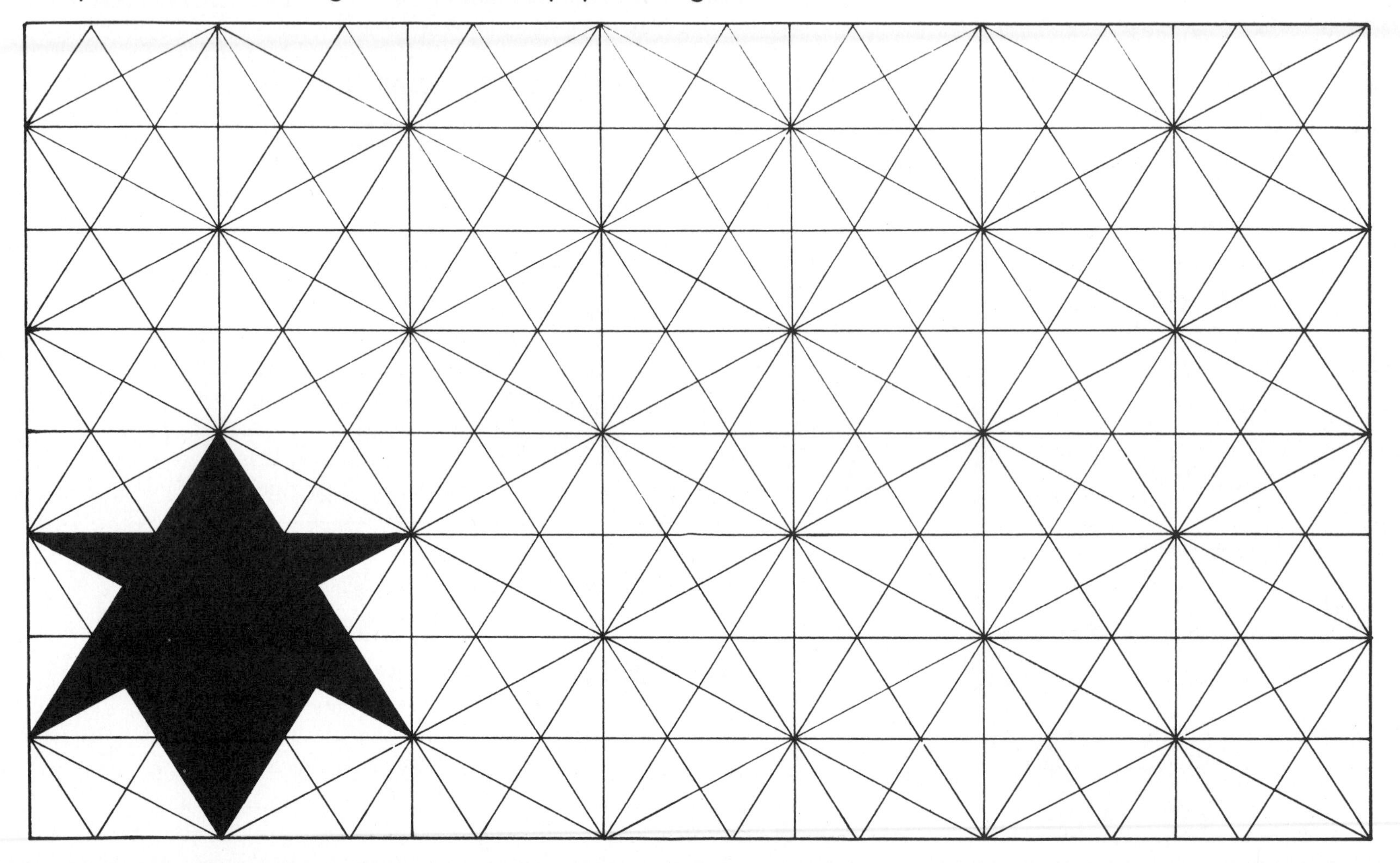

Name ____________________

Party invitations

Below is an invitation card for a Christmas party.

✤ Look at it carefully to see what information it contains and what else is needed.

✤ Now design your own invitation in the space below.

Name ____________________

Make a postal van

Make a postal van

✤ Design and make a moving van that the postman could use to deliver Christmas cards and gifts.
You can use any of the following items:

- cardboard boxes
- garden cane
- drawing pins
- ice-cream carton
- cotton reels
- drinks cans
- wooden dowel
- scissors
- adhesive
- craft knife

My design

✤ Plan your vehicle in the space opposite. Make a list of things you will need. Can you use a motor to make it move?

✤ After making your vehicle, evaluate it – how could it be improved? What problems did you have?
What would you do differently if you made it again?

Name ____________________

Toy-making machine

Santa's elves need a machine to help them make the toys.

✤ Design a machine or robot that can do all these things:

• cut • paste • measure • assemble • staple • wrap/box • label

✤ Use this space to draw your design. Use the back of this sheet if you need more space.

My design

Name ____________

A new sleigh for Santa

Santa is bored with his old-fashioned sleigh! He wants a new one, so he has sent off a list of what he would like to the sleigh factory.

✤ Design a new sleigh making sure you include everything Santa wants.

Old sleigh

What I would like in my new sleigh:

- a different shape, designed to go faster
- retractable wheels for land use
- more comfortable seats
- headlamps for night driving
- bright, bold paintwork
- something to slow sleigh quickly in emergencies
- to be able to float for water use

Yours,

Santa

My design

Name ____________________

Name ____________

Advent calendar 2

Advent calendar 2

- Colour the nativity scene and cut along the dotted lines.
- Draw and colour pictures in the boxes on this page.
- Place the nativity scene page over this page, then stick it together around the edges.
- Number the doors from 1 to 24.

Name ____________________

Make a pop-up Christmas card

✤ Colour in the pictures.
✤ Cut out the card outline and the figure of Santa.
✤ Carefully cut along the dotted lines.
✤ Fold the paper along line A away from you, then push the small section with dotted lines out towards you, creasing firmly along the lines so that it stands out like a step.
✤ Stick Santa to the bottom half of this section. Be careful not to get any glue on the top half.
✤ Fold downwards along line B so that the words 'Merry Christmas' are on the front. Santa should now pop up as the card opens.
✤ Write your own Christmas greeting inside.

Name ________________

Make a stained glass window

Make a stained glass window

✤ Trace this design on to black card then carefully cut out the words and shapes. Stick coloured Cellophane to the back. Hang the stained glass against a window so that the light shines through.

Name ____________________

Make a lantern

✤ Draw and colour a Christmas scene in the space opposite.
✤ Cut out the rectangle and fold in half.
✤ Cut along the dotted lines.

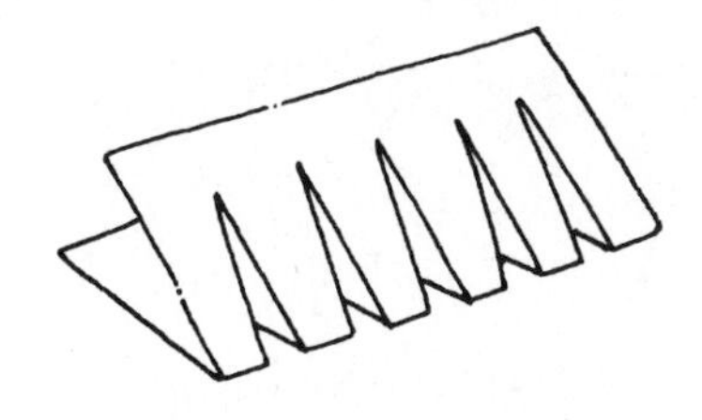

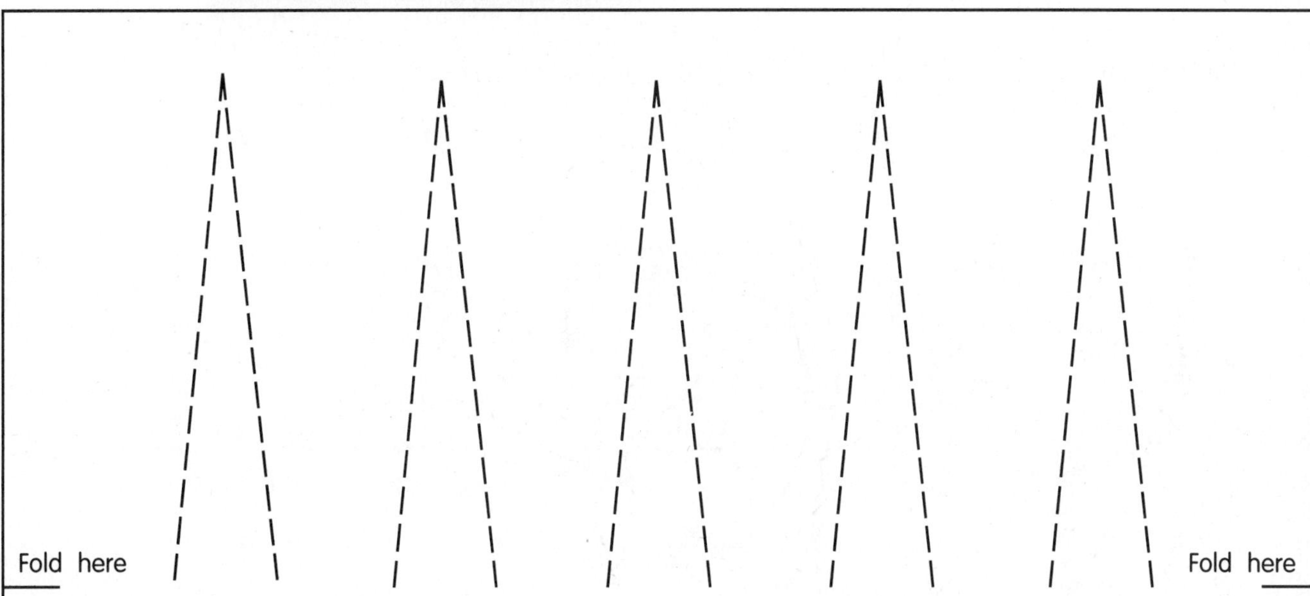

✤ Form a cylinder by glueing the top and bottom corners together.
✤ Staple a strip of paper over the top to make a handle.

Name ______________________

Christmas bookmarks

Christmas bookmarks

✤ Trace these designs on to card, then colour them and cut them out.

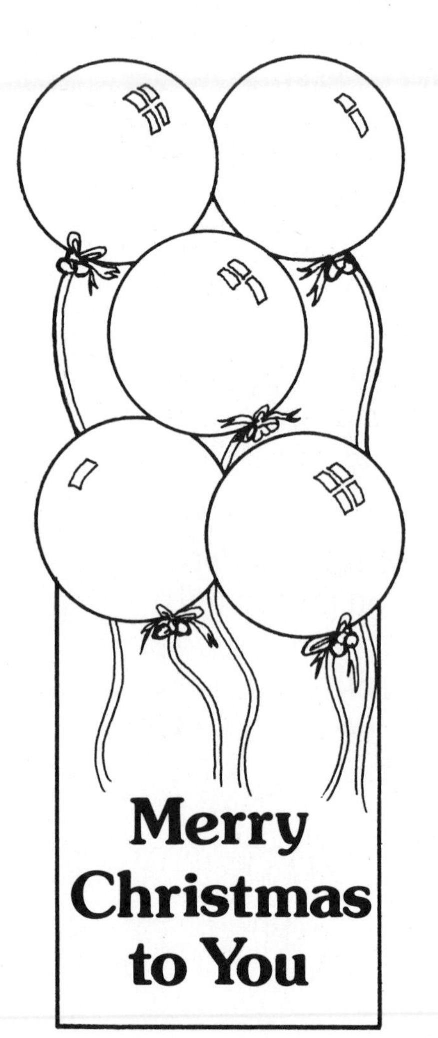

Name ____________________

Make a basket

✤ Cut out the basket and the handle.
✤ Decorate the outside of the basket.
✤ Fold along the dotted lines. Make it into a basket, sticking the side flaps as shown below.
✤ Stick the handle to the basket.
✤ Fill the basket with sweets or small toys and give it to a friend for Christmas.

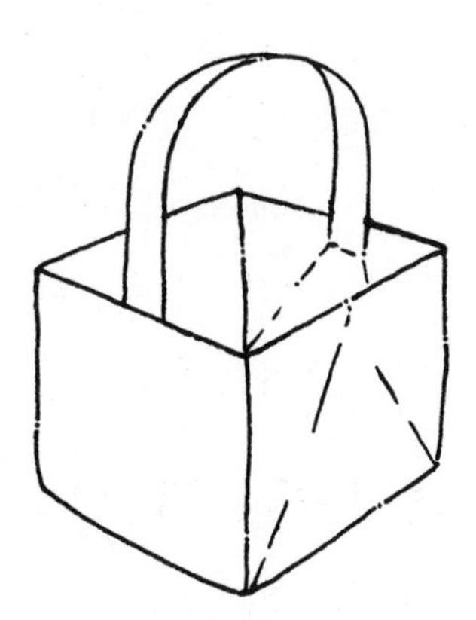

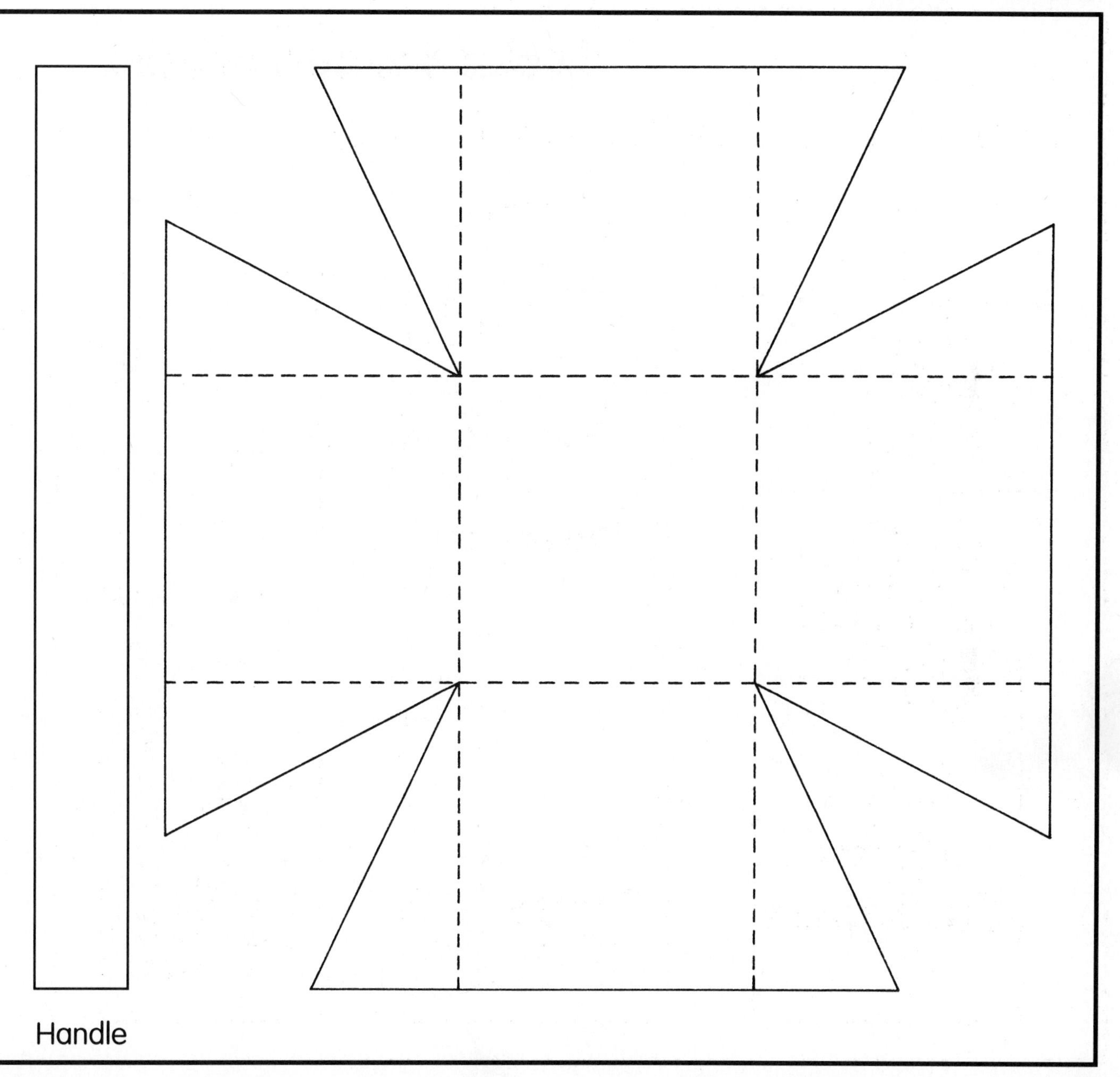

Name ____________________

Make a Santa mobile

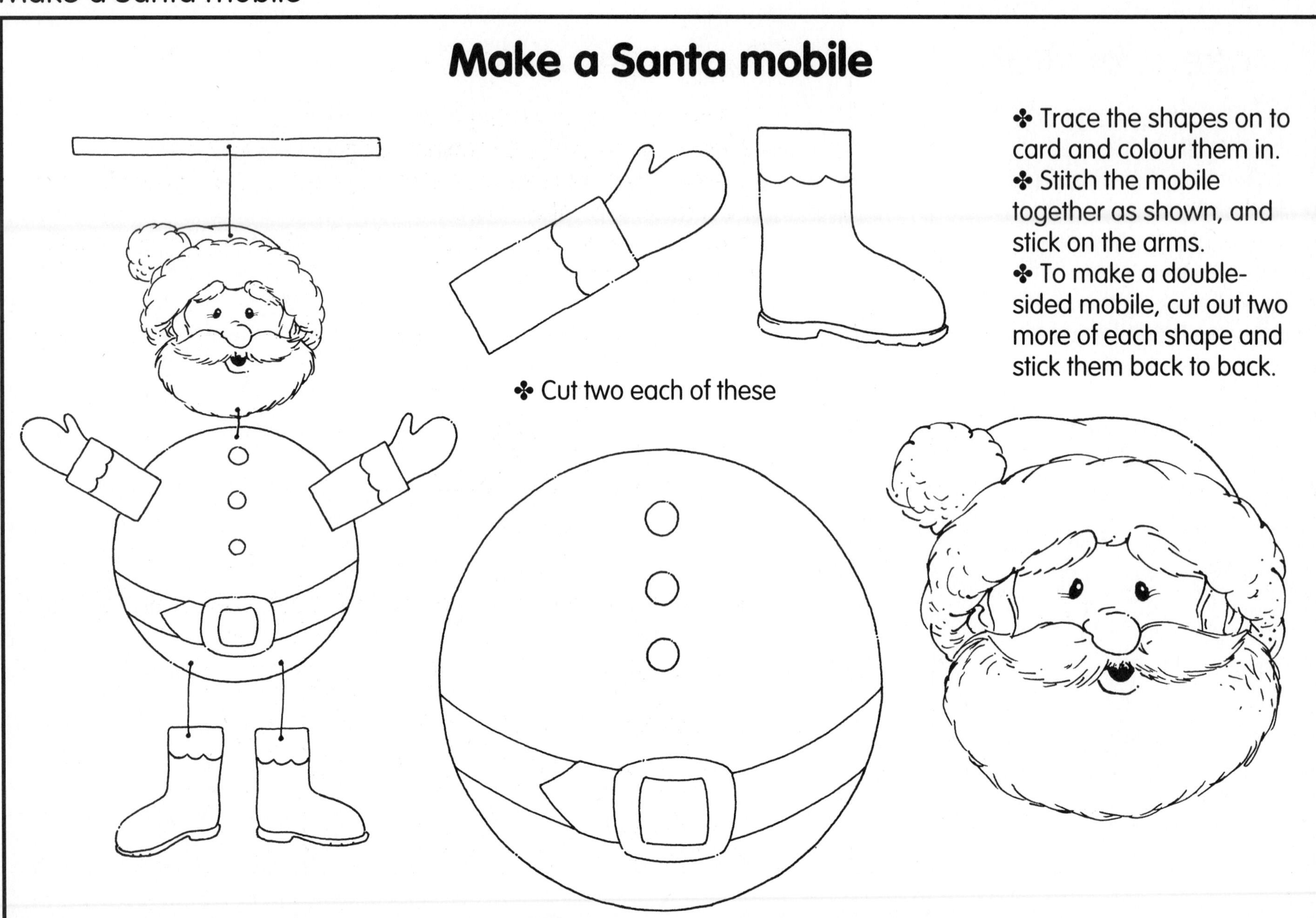

Name ________________

Making decorations

✤ Trace the diamond shape on to black paper and cut it out.
✤ Remove the centre by cutting along the dotted lines.
✤ Stick a piece of coloured Cellophane or tissue paper behind it to create a stained-glass effect.
✤ Make several diamonds and put them together to make stars or other Christmas shapes.

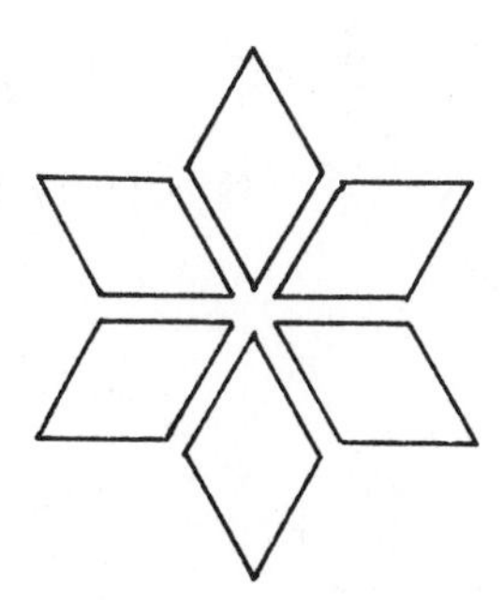

✤ Alternatively, colour each diamond in bright shapes and patterns.

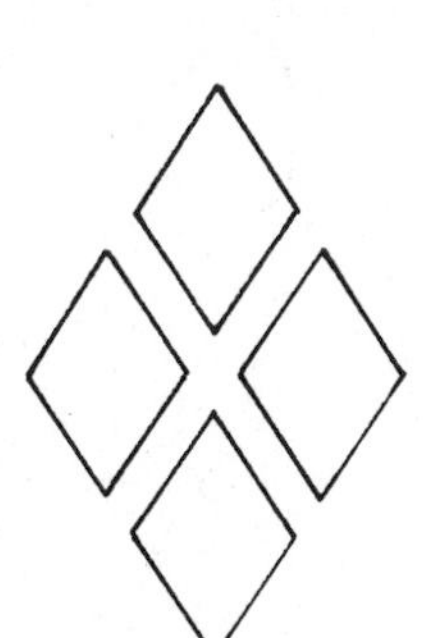

Name ______________________

Make a nativity scene 1

Name ____________________

Make a nativity scene 2

- ✤ Trace these shapes on to card. Cut them out along the dotted lines.
- ✤ Decorate the body then colour it.
- ✤ Fold the body to form a cone, then stick it together at Point A.
- ✤ Attach the head (and wings when making the angel).
- ✤ Use scrap materials to decorate the characters. Use knitting yarn for beards and sparkling fabric for the angel's halo.

A

Body

Head

Angel's wing

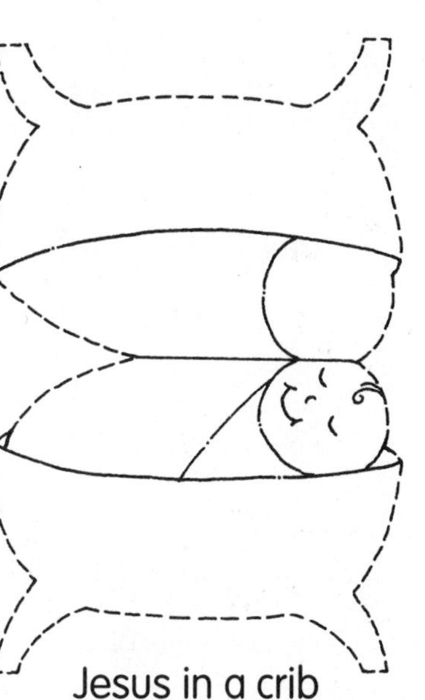
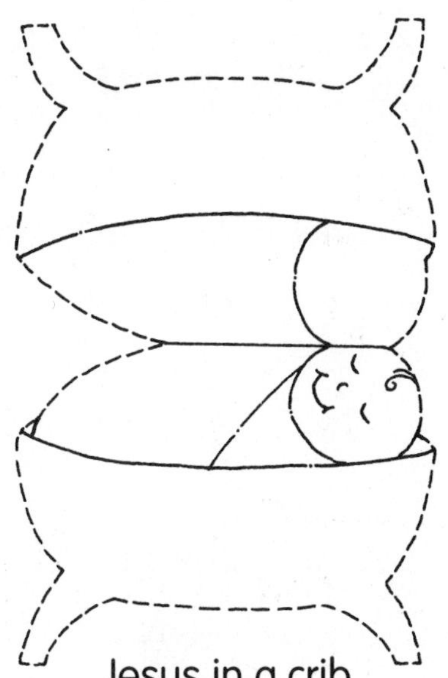

Jesus in a crib

Joseph

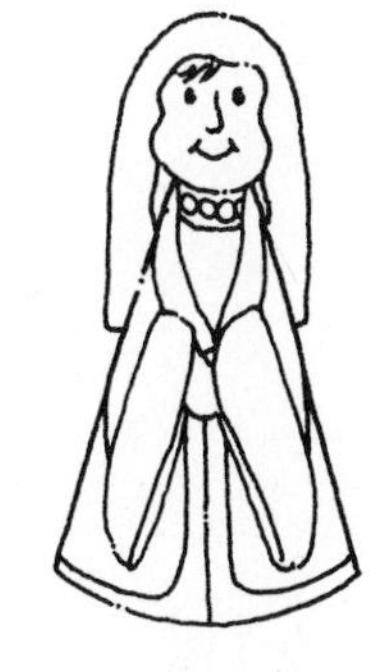

Mary

Angel

Name ____________________

Make a nativity scene 3

Name ____________________

Christmas alphabet

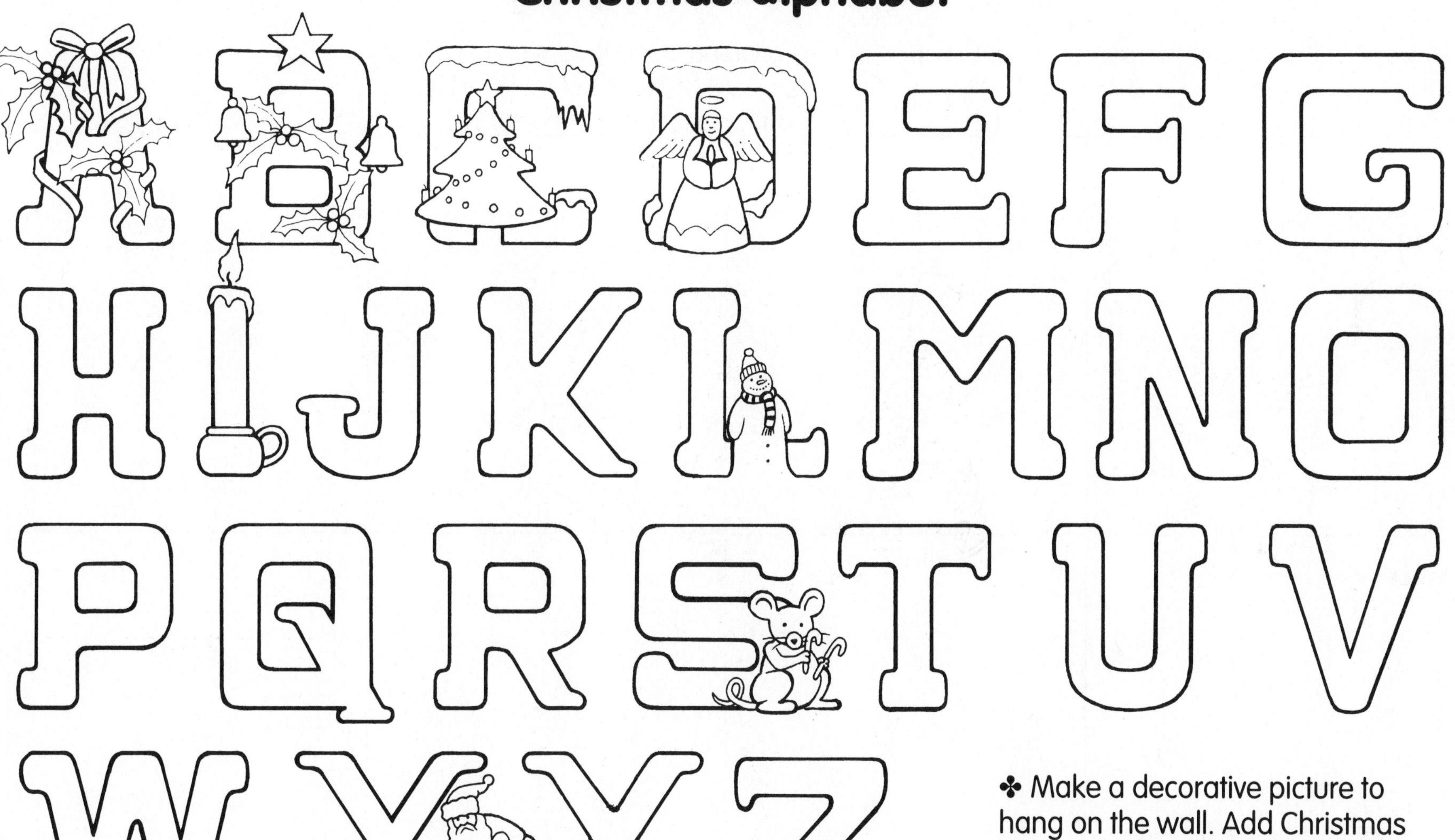

✤ Make a decorative picture to hang on the wall. Add Christmas designs to each letter, then colour them in. The first four letters have been done for you.

Name ______________

Christmas wrapping

✤ Repeat the design in each square. Colour it in and cut it out. Use it as wrapping paper.

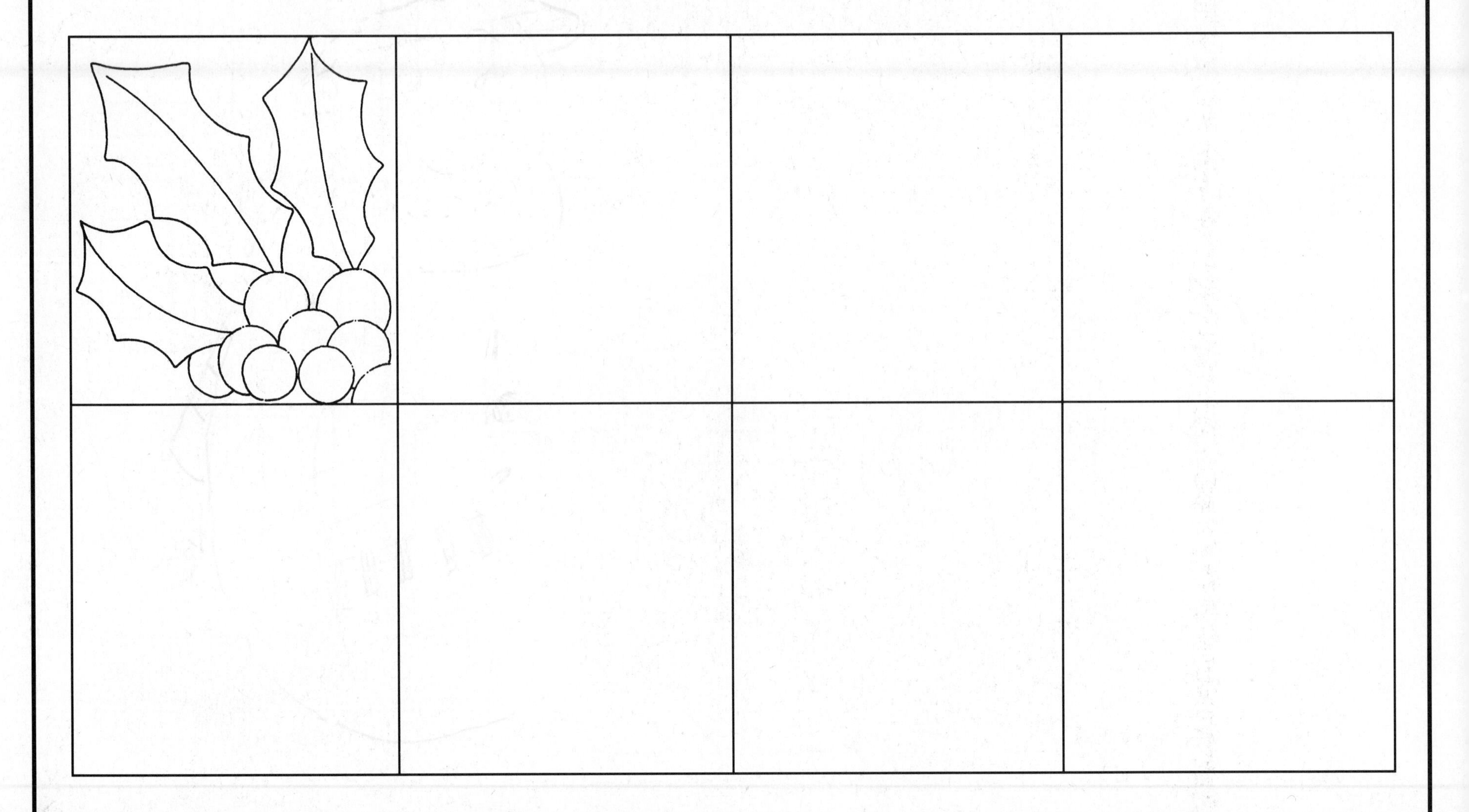

Name ________________

Nativity scene

Name ____________________

Snowman and wreath

Name ____________________

Ox and Joseph

Name ______________

Robin and church

Name ____________________

Gingerbread man and turkey

Name ____________________

Donkey and sheep

Name ____________________

Angel and shepherd

Name ______________

The three kings

Name ____________________

Reindeer and elf

Name ____________________

Tree and santa

Name ___________________

Crib and Mary

Name ________________

Stocking and bauble

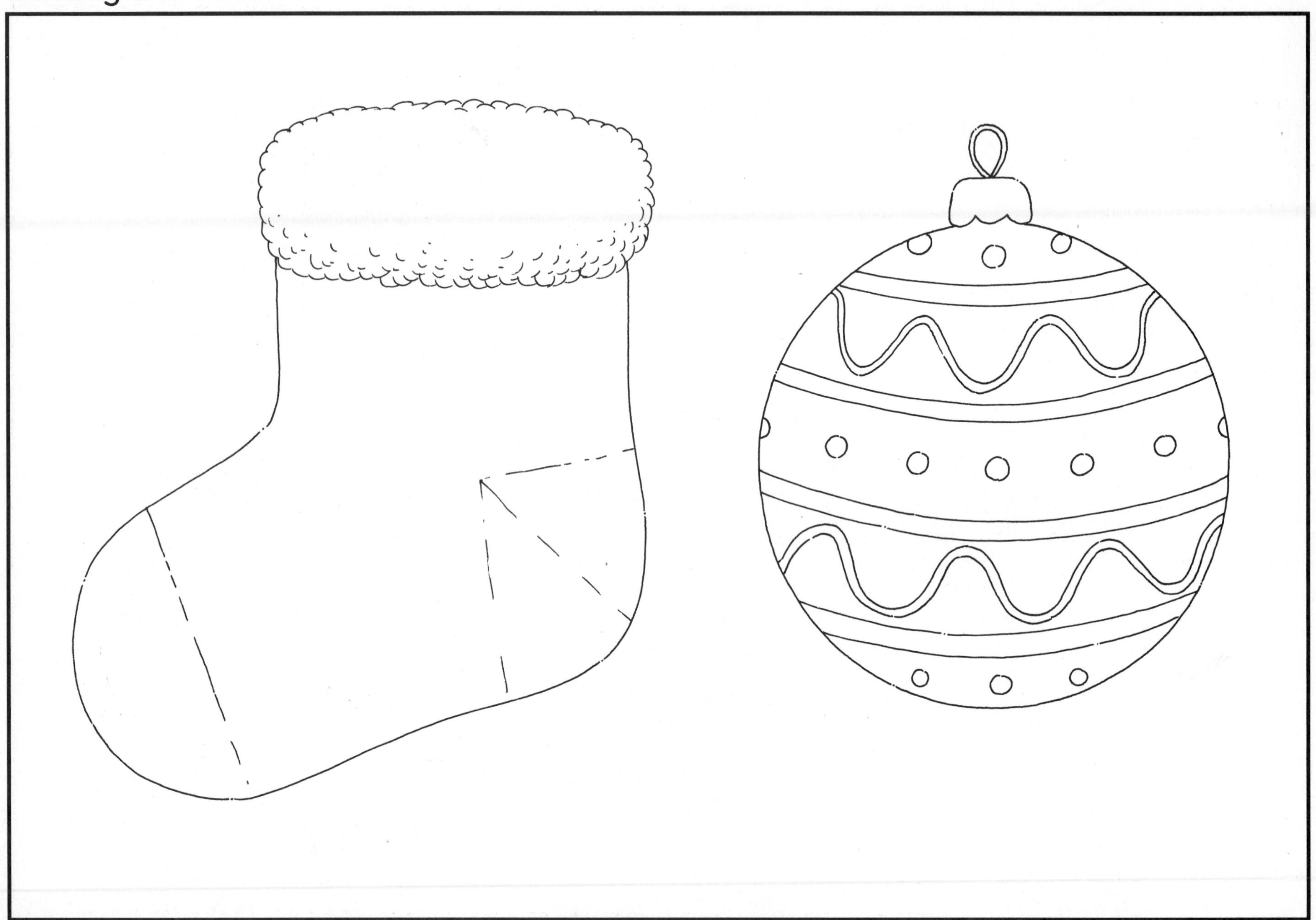

Name ____________________

Holly and pudding

Name ____________________

Bell and cracker

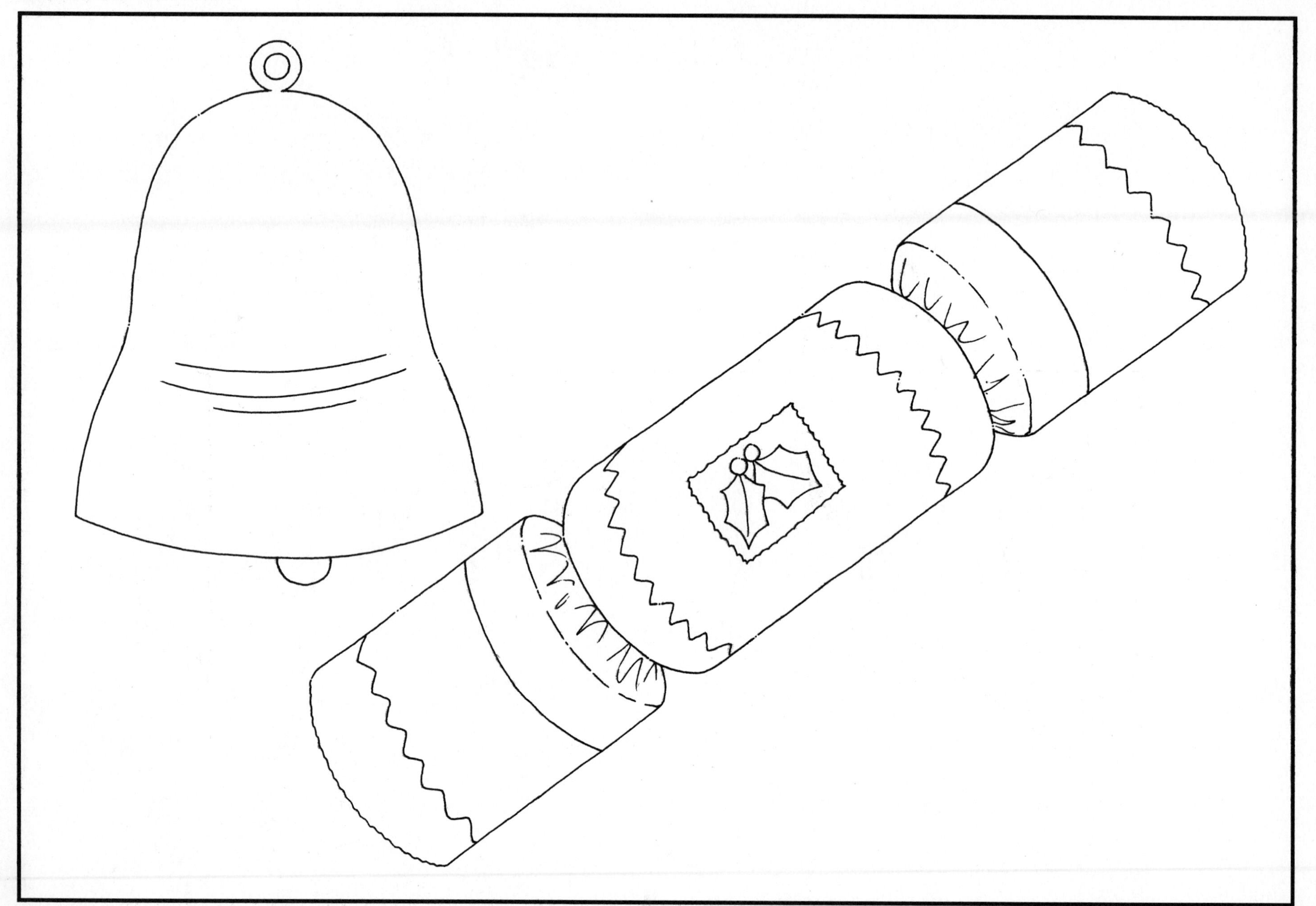

Name ______________________

Star and candle

Name ____________

Christmas jigsaw

✤ Cut out these shapes and join them together to make a picture.